Write Where We Are

WriteOn Joliet Sixth Annual Anthology 2022

By WriteOn Joliet

Cover art by Sue Mydliak

Cover art by Sue Mydliak

ISBN: 978-1-949777-49-9
writeonjoliet.com

2

WriteOn Joliet anthology 2022 contributors: Denise M. Baran-Unland, Ed Calkins, Kathy Carberry ,Holly Coop, Steven James Cordin, Diana Estell, Robert B. Hafey, Tom Hernandez, Sharon Houk, Lindsay Lake, Cean Magosky, James Moore, Sue Mydliak, Colleen H. Robbins, Jennifer Russ, Duanne Walton

We create life, bring life, give life, sing life through our words,
Precious golden nuggets of pain and joy, birds soaring and diving
Dipping and climbing high, higher, highest Until neither the eye
nor the sky can hold them anymore. Like birds. Our words.- Tom
Hernandez

ABOUT WRITEON JOLIET

WriteOn started as WriteOn Minooka, co-founded by Denise M. Baran-Unland and Kristina Skaggs. Our members come from all over the southern suburbs.

Some have self-published or have been traditionally published. Others are still exploring their writing options and interests. Regardless of our place in the writing world, WriteOn welcomes everyone looking to write, read and grow.

WriteOn Joliet is a welcoming, diverse group of writers of varied skills, interests and experience. The group includes professional journalists, fiction novelists, bloggers, screenwriters, musicians and poets.

We promise a safe, comfortable and supportive atmosphere to share your work, and constructive feedback so that everyone can benefit from our shared knowledge.

WriteOn is a dues-paying organization. The first visit is free.

For more information, visit writeonJoliet.com.

TABLE OF CONTENTS

A DOSE OF HOPE

By Robert B. Hafey

I need a dose of hope. It's not that I am hopeless, but after enduring two years of a neutered life, thanks to a global pandemic, I need the promise that hope brings. Two vaccine doses, followed by a booster, allowed me to begin to think hopefully. Yet, if I am honest with myself, the pandemic highlighted that I live in a country characterized by selfishness and individualism, rather than compassion and a general concern for each other. This realization has taken a toll on me. Being compassionate is deeply embedded in the double spiral of my DNA, and I have discovered I am incompatible with those who lack the compassion gene.

Then recently, as I doom-scrolled through the news headlines on my cell phone, I learned a compassionless madman ordered the invasion of Ukraine, and yet another new COVID variant is advancing faster than his Russian army on Kyiv. Disgust, or simply my form of burying my head in the sand, causes me to vow once again to stop reading the news. I realize my occasional lack of hope is often a result of my cell phone addiction. To delay the next fix, I turn to a self-help treatment I dispense almost daily. I put my phone into solitary confinement, a zippered pocket, and go hiking.

As I walk, with camera in hand, the world slows down. "Ah, this is just what I need," I mumble to myself.

My mind quickly becomes fixated on the flora and fauna around me. Capturing the natural world in photographs is one of my passions. I soon notice maple trees, full of reddish buds, breaking up the almost colorless dull gray and brown March landscape. Hiking on this same trail, multiple times a week, allows me to observe the slow process of natural change. Soon enough, the maples will be covered in fluttering glossy green leaves. Nature is patient. Change takes time.

I begin to think about the connection between time, and my impatience with people and a society clearly off the rails.

"With time, is all change possible?" I ask myself.

In times of trouble people used to pull together. You know, the tornado tears through town and the residents' differences were temporarily forgotten as they pull together to help those in need. A global tornado, the pandemic, is responsible for almost a million deaths in our country. This politicized pandemic, rather than pull us together, is tearing us apart. Misinformed people who refuse the vaccine, continue to contract, help spread, and die from the virus.

"What are they thinking?" I mumble to myself.

Progressing forward I feel myself get into the steady rhythm of my walk. My mind begins to calm down until something causes me to jerk to a stop. My eyes catch a glimpse of an animal running from my left. It looks like a dachshund, with the face of a seal and a fat long tapered tail. I quickly grab my camera, look through the viewfinder, and press the shutter just as the critter leaps onto and over a concrete barrier wall, that lines the opposite side of the trail. My heart races as I fumble to press the correct buttons to preview the images. What I see are three beautiful, almost identical, photos of the concrete barrier. Disappointed, I stand there reviewing the only image I managed to capture, a clear mental image of a river otter.

Moving forward on the trail I begin another discussion with myself. This is, sadly, another unsettling outcome of the pandemic.

"A river otter! Can you believe it?" Never in my lifetime did I expect to see a river otter in or near the Des Plaines River.

"How is this possible?" I mumble. For much of my childhood, and all my adult life, I have lived within a few miles of the Des Plaines. It, like many rivers, became a place for corporations and others to dump their waste and trash. Just a few decades ago the Des Plaines River had been a silted up, smelly, almost lifeless body of water.

When heavy rains cause the river to swell and flood the lowland areas along it banks, debris floats in and stays when the water recedes. As I walk past, I see plastic waste of all kinds, along with the occasional tire. The sins of the past are clearly visible in the now naked leafless woodland.

I vaguely remember that about fifty years ago the Clean Water Act made its way through the legislature. Our country, and its politicians, had said, enough is enough. This fact proved, that in our past, we as a country could work together for a common good.

After a moment of hopefulness, my mind quickly drifts to lead water pipes, and water unfit for human consumption, in Flint, Michigan. Oh, my now agitated mind continues, there is this current problem called global warming that many politicians refuse to acknowledge or act upon. "What are those bastards waiting for!"

As I traipse forward, and get back into my hiking rhythm, my blood pressure begins to moderate. Soon I pass the spot, where late last summer, I had seen and taken photos of a bald eagle. When it happened, I was giddy with excitement. Later in the fall, after the leaves had floated to the ground, someone on the trail pointed out an eagle's nest about two hundred yards off the trail. Now, five months later, as I stare through the wooded landscape, in the distance I again locate the huge wooden branch structure. Peering through my camera's 300mm telephoto lens, I see the unmistakable white head and large yellow beak of an adult bald eagle in the center of the nest. "She must be sitting on eggs!" I comment.

As a child, I dreamt of seeing a bald eagle, and now they are nesting along the Des Plaines River. Both otters and eagles require a steady source of food, from clean water, to breed and survive. Nature is patient. Change takes time.

I move forward while trying to stay focused on nature, rather than the state of the world. A mile up the trail I see a man fishing.

Craving small talk, like everyone else in our locked-down pandemic world, I ask, "Catch anything?"

"A couple of northern pike and a smallie."

"That's awesome! Northern pike in this river?" I exclaimed.

"Yeah, I have been catching them here for a few years. It is amazing how clean the water is now."

He continues, "I recently read that there are now about sixteen species of fish living in the Des Plaines, up from a low of just two to four a few decades ago."

As we finish chatting, I turn to leave and shout, "Good luck."

11

Another half-mile up the trail, I see a small animal running toward me. Looking inquisitive, hopeful, confident, focused, and a little cocky, it moves steadily forward on its never ending search for the next meal.

I freeze in place and slowly raise my camera. As I look through the viewfinder, it stops, and we begin a stare down. I snap multiple photos before it quickly turns and leaps over the barrier wall. I excitedly preview my photos.

"Wow, that is a mink, and it is cute as hell," I mumble.

Standing in the middle of the trail, I grin as I again scroll through the images of the mink on my camera's preview screen. In each photo, the daylight reflects off the mink's nose and the tips of its chocolate brown fur like tiny beacons of hope.

I feel renewed, and a bit hopeful, so I turn and begin my two mile hike back to the trailhead. Nature had again delivered a booster dose of relief. The presence of an otter, a bald eagle, game fish, and a mink, now again living in what had been a wasteland, made it clear that nature has what I do not.

An abundance of time and patience.

AN EMPTY WIN

By Tom Hernandez

Thanks to you
I may die a death unexpected
But before, I will also
Cry tears of joy uncried
Dance dances undanced
Spread my arms wider than ever
Seek and welcome new voices
Ride a train with new passengers
Sing songs unsung
To celebrate a new love
That will last a lifetime
Death will not be your victory
But rather a chance to mark a life well lived
Filled with love and passion
Beauty and blessings
Gratitude and grace
I do not welcome you
But neither do I fear
Because I entrust my Tomorrow
My soul
My being
To those who have carried me
Past your dark doorstep
You may get my body
But I keep my spirit

7-10-22

BICYCLE GRASS

By Colleen H. Robbins

The rusty blue VW bug's tires screeched as it ran off the road. A dozen children on bicycles straggled their way around the curve.

"Tourists!" The group of children laughed as Jessica's mother struggled to regain the road.

The VW chugged its way back onto the pavement and rounded another curve. Two turns and a driveway into a parking lot later, the car wheezed and stalled with a BANG. The doors popped open as Jessica and her mother got out.

"Ten feet, Mom! I get to drive again!" Jess climbed in on the driver's side as her mother pushed. The girl steered the car neatly into a parking space, then stretched her foot down to stomp on the brake. Her mother reached in and set the emergency brake. Jess scrambled out again.

The motel looked like the last place they'd lived in New Jersey: cracked parking lot, trash on the sidewalk, and peeling paint. A buzzing, half-lit sign swung in the breeze.

PACIFIC SHORES MOTEL
V CANCiES
MONT LY RATES AVAIL

The breeze shifted, and she smelled the ocean. Jess followed her nose to the rocky shoreline behind the motel. The waves rolled in long swells, some curling onto the thin sandy strip and others crashing over the rocks. Long tangles of seaweed stretched along the water's edge like dark green crime-scene tape.

Jess wrinkled her nose. The water smelled wrong. Seaweed and iodine, like home, but also an underlying oily smell. Jess shuddered. It smelled like the hair of the boy who hit her at school last week.

All because of the squid whales. She got in trouble every time she talked about them, or about the dreams where they talked to her. All she did was draw a picture of one with a little island next to it, and the tentacles all waving around the open head. It was a good picture. Her teacher hung it in the hallway. Stupid sixth grader blamed her for his bad dreams. Just not fair.

"Red-haired witch," the boy had hissed. "You made me dream about your picture, and your stupid monster ate me." He punched her before she could say a word, and didn't stop until the gym teacher pulled him off.

"Jessica, come help me with the suitcases. We're in 11A." Her mother's voice broke her out of the memory. Her ribs still hurt.

"Coming, Mom." She shuffled back around to the car and grabbed her two suitcases. The small one filled with notebooks and crayons banged into the ground, cracking a wheel. The other rolled nicely along on its leash. It's like an orange puppy with big pink flowers. I want a pet.

"Mom, look." Baskets of twisted grass hung on every curtain rod, and were nailed around every door.

"Wow, a decorator must have lived here before. They're pretty enough, we can keep them."

Jess abandoned her suitcases in the living room to check out the rest of the apartment. "I get my own bedroom! Can I have a window? "

"Pick whichever. Tomorrow we'll get you in school."

She dreamed of squid whales. Little ones the size of baby seals, with wet velvety skins. They brought her shiny stones and treasures from sunken ships. When they all clustered around her, she could see an empty spot.

"Who is missing?"

"Our brother. They took him away. He's so hungry."

"What does he eat?"

"What do you eat?"

Jess woke to the smell of bacon and eggs. She ate everything on her plate, and wanted more.

"Someone's hungry this morning. Ready for school?"

"Hungry, yes. School, not really."

"I'm sure the school will be different here."

"I'm still gonna get teased. Can we dye my hair first?"

Her mother took the dishes. "You're too young to dye your hair. Besides, you have beautiful hair. It's just like your father's."

School turned out better than Jess expected. So few children lived in Pacific Shores that classrooms held several grades each: Kindergarten through Second grade in room 1, Third and Fourth in room 2, and Fifth through Eighth in room 3.

Best of all, four of the boys in her class had red hair. Not her bright orangey-red, but reddish-blonde and brown with dark red mixed in.

At recess, Jess hung back from the group. Everyone played with their friends, and no one spoke to her at all except Ms. Martin, her teacher. Probably because I'm new.

After recess, Jess relaxed. Maybe Mom was right. Maybe everything would be okay.

"Art time, students. Jessica, I want you to paint. Everyone else at your current projects. When Jess stood in front of the third easel, Ms. Martin leaned over. "Paint the ocean."

Jess painted the ocean from the side, with sharks and fish in different depths, and lobsters and crabs on the bottom. She decided to add a dolphin. She dipped the brush in gray paint.

"Hey, you're the tourist girl, aren't you." A boy's voice spoke loudly behind her.

She jumped. The brush flew out of her hand and splattered across the bottom of the picture. A particularly large drip trembled on the page, threatening the floor. Jess reached out her hand to catch it just as the boy jostled her arm.

"I said, you're the tourist girl," the boy with brown and dark red hair repeated.

Jess shrugged his hand off and looked at her picture. Her fingers had smeared the drip sideways. It looked like tentacles. She stepped back and looked again. The splatter looked like a squid whale.

Panicked, she backed away from the easel. Her mother would never believe the picture was an accident.

"Are you done, dear? Peter, leave her alone." Ms. Martin picked up the picture and looked at it. "Excellent, dear. I think I'll

16

show the principal." She walked out of the room before Jess could say anything.

Horrified, Jessica remained silent for the next hour. She bolted out of class when the bell rang and ran down the road.

"Where's that tourist girl?" Pete asked somewhere behind her.

She dove behind a bush. It took almost twenty minutes for the swarm of bicycles to pass. Brightly painted, each bicycle had a handful of grass streaming from each side of the handlebars.

After crouching for half an hour more, she followed the signs to the hotels and beach. She walked down the marked beach access and stood, staring.

On this side of town, a sandy beach stretched down to the water's edge. Knots of dark green seaweed and occasional tree trunks dotted the sand. Past the beach access, small dunes topped with sharp-edged dune grass made a barrier between the hotels and the sand.

She almost tripped over the signpost at the bottom of the access.

> This beach is part of a protected wildlife park.
> It is illegal to disturb seals, sea lions, and
> other marine mammals.
> If you see a baby seal or other mammal,
> do not approach.
> Return to your hotel and call
> the Visitor Center immediately.
> Trained park personnel will remove them.

The Visitor Center. Jess sought it out and found her mother behind the cash register, wearing a hideous beige vest sprinkled with glitter-glued pink seashells.

"Done with school? Not so bad, I bet."

"Mostly okay, I guess."

"Walk on home and we'll talk later. I might even have a surprise."

17

Later that evening, a pick-up truck almost as rusty as the VW dropped Jessica's mother off. When she came inside, she wheeled in a pretty little pink bicycle with multicolored strands of plastic decorating the handlebars and a white wicker basket.

"It's a little small, but you can get back and forth to school on it."

"Thanks, Mom!" Jess hugged her mother. She practiced with the bicycle until dark. When her mom went inside, she peeled off the masking tape price tag inside the chain guard: $3.00 . Scratched olive paint peeked out under the tape.

Jess explored the sandy beach in her sleep, looking at a huge stump the water stranded high on the sand. The inside was completely hollow, and tall enough to almost stand. The hole got smaller as she crawled on hands and knees to the far end. Jess could barely squeeze through. When she did, she was surrounded by baby squid-whales. Their sluglike trails stretched back through the sand to the water's edge.

Saturday morning Jess rode her new bicycle to the beach. Many of the older children rode up and down the edge of the wet sand. Jess tried the same, surprised at how steady she rode.

Peter skidded to a halt directly in front of her. "If it isn't the tourist girl with her shiny new tourist bike." He dismounted and handed his old blue bike off to another boy, then knocked Jess off of hers. He grabbed the plastic streamers and yanked them loose from the handlebars. "My sister would like these."

Another boy came up and yanked her basket loose. He crumbled the wicker between his hands. "Not very sturdy."

"Too small for you, too." Peter lifted the pink bike overhead and ran down to the water. He threw it as far as he could. The water curled around the bicycle, swirling sand and shells. The bicycle slowly sank into the ground with each wave. The boys rode off, laughing.

Jess waded out and grabbed her handlebars. The wave came and swirled around her legs, sucking her feet deeper. Terrified, she dug at the wet sand and yanked as hard as she could, then kicked her feet free of the sand as she slowly pulled the bicycle free. By the time she dragged it ashore, the pink paint was scratched and sand stuck to the pedals and chain.

She could hear Peter's laughter from the direction of the beach access, so she wheeled the bicycle up to the dunes and hid it in the grass. A tree stump lay on its side further down the beach. I wonder if it's hollow? She ran to take a look.

Awed by the size of the tree stump - fully as big as the one in her dream - she looked inside for her little escape hatch. The same narrowing tube, except for a lot more sand and shells. She turned with arms wide to welcome the baby squid-whales.

A squid whale humped up the beach toward her, but this one was no baby. More than six feet across, its head split into dozens of eight foot long tentacles. Jess scrambled backwards, deeper into the trunk. A tentacle followed her and grabbed her leg.

"Ouch!" Instead of the velvety skin she'd been expecting, the tentacle oozed slime that stung her leg like a thousand jellyfish. She grabbed a shell from beneath her feet and cut at the tentacle.

The squid-whale hissed and backed away. The tentacle retracted into its body.

Jess waved the shell at the creature. "Leave me alone or I'll cut them all off." She sensed its anger just before the squid-whale charged.

Tentacles snapping around her, Jess wiggled into her escape hatch. The entire stump heaved as the squid-whale tried to force its way in, but it was too wide. Jess scrambled faster, worried that her escape hatch might be blocked by the sand if the stump rolled.

Another tentacle brushed the bottom of her foot, leaving more slime as she scrambled out the small end. She took off running toward the dunes as the stump lifted off the ground with the squid-whales efforts to free itself. Looking back over her shoulder, she tripped over her bicycle and sprawled across the razor sharp saw grass.

The creature freed itself and humped its way after Jess. She closed her eyes, legs still tangled with the bicycle.

And opened them a minute later when the squid whale whined like a hurt dog. It threw its body back and forth on the sand's edge near the dune grass.

Down the beach came more laughter, and Peter's faint shout. "Hey tourist girl."

The squid-whale froze. It looked at Jess, and she could feel its hunger. Then it looked down the beach toward Peter. A moment later, it humped its way down the beach, moving faster than Jess could have run on a good day.

She noticed it swerve to avoid a patch of dune grass that stretched a little further down the sand. She stood up, righted her bicycle, and stuffed a handful of grass strands into each handlebar base. Afterward, she pedaled carefully down the packed sand. As she approached the squid-whale, it backed away.

Jess carefully ignored the bloody thing the squid-whale dragged toward the water, though she did recognize Peter's bicycle laying across the sand in the squid whale's track. His old blue bicycle, with the brand new plastic streamers poking out from the handlebars where she now proudly had dune grass.

CORNELL DYER AND THE CALCIUM DEFICIENT BONES

By Denise M. Baran-Unland

When supernatural super sleuth Cornell Dyer finds himself between sleuthing jobs, he fills the time by teaching science while the real teacher is ill. But in a school that's supposedly getting remodeled, Cornell encounters one mystery after another: vanishing classroom skeletons, plants that come and go, and a piano for every student. Cornell is certain his classroom holds the answer – and that he is one of the clues.

She glanced up from her stack of papers and looked at the wall clock. Fifteen more minutes.

Then she could collect her third grade students' unit tests on the human body.

She stretched her thin, crooked fingers – achy and stiff from holding a pen so long – and brushed back a lock of wispy white hair.

A few noises broke the room's silence – like the tick tick tick tick tick of the timer as it wound down.

Like the tapping of Davy's left foot, a sign he was thinking deeply.

Like the scritch of Janey's teeth against the metal of her pink pencil eraser, a sign she was thinking deeply.

Like Timmy clearing his throat over and over and over again, a sign he was thinking deeply.

Like the scrape of the legs of the old maple wood chair across the old mastic tile, for Carl never could sit still.

Only Susie made no noise. She just twirled a pigtail and bit her lip, signs she was thinking deeply.

BING!

All seventeen students set down their pencils.

The end-of-the-day bell rang through the intercom.

"Class," she said. "Please set your tests on my desk as you

leave."

The students rose. They shuffled to the front of the room. They placed their tests on her desk and then dashed out the door.

She picked up the papers, straightened them, and then slid the stack into her duffle bag. Then she roamed the room,

She lined up every desk and chair with the seams of the tile.

She clicked off the overhead projector.

She tugged the pull ring dangling from the world map and gently retracted it into place.

She picked up the chalkboard eraser and erased her stick figure drawings. She set the eraser in the chalkboard tray and placed the pieces of chalk next to it.

Then she snapped off the lights and hung up her work.

The next day, the first period students waited and waited and waited for their teacher. Finally, Craig and Jenny went to the principal's office.

"Why are you here?" Mr. Principal demanded. "Why aren't you in class?"

"Our teacher is gone," Craig said.

"She never showed up," Jenny added.

Mr. Principal leaned over his desk and called into the next room. "Miss School Secretary, please print dittos for the fifth grade science students. And please sit with them in class.

"Yes, Mr. Principal," Miss School Secretary said.

Soon, Miss School Secretary was leaving the school office with Craig, Jenny, and a handful of dittos. That's when Mr. Principal reached for the phone.

"Is this the world famous supernatural super sleuth Cornell Dyer? Do you specialize in Amulets, Fortune-Telling (with and without cards), Ghost-Hunting, Horoscopes, Numerology, Palm-Reading, Potions, Séances, Spells, Vampire-Slaying, controlling zambie populations, and deactivating Moravian pink goblins and cold whispers? Great! I need a substitute teacher. Please come right away!"

It was late afternoon when Cornell Dyer drove his motor home past the "Welcome to Sunnystorm, Pennsylvania" sign.

What a long, long drive!

Traffic jams!

Stops for breakfast, morning snack, lunch, first afternoon snack, and second afternoon snack.

Road constructions!

Plus, read up on Sunnystorm, just in case he stumbled upon a supernatural mystery.

He learned Sunnystorm wasn't a big town. In fact, the town only had one school for grade school and high school.

But Sunnystorm was a nice town with nice people who earned plenty of money. But it wasn't always that way.

Sunnystorm used to be a poor town. Sunnystorm struggled to survive – until it's luck changed.

Today Sunnystorm was full of people with plenty of money. And these people wanted to pay Cornell lots of money. People with lots of money were Cornell's favorite kind of people.

That's why Cornell agreed to teach when his real job was solving supernatural mysteries.

Cornell turned on his wipers to swish away the pattering rain. He also lowered the visor to keep the sun out of his eyes.

Sunnystorm, Cornell snorted. They sure got the name right.

He read each street sign as he passed it. Where was Hitchcrook Lane? Ah, there it was, just past the traffic light.

Soon Cornell was turning into the school parking lot right behind the garbage truck, which drove to the rear of the building. Cornell, on the other hand, stopped his very large motor home right in front of the school. The building had three stories and was made of old yellow bricks. It had tall vertical windows with old, stained window shades, the kind of shades that teachers pulled down by white plastic rings. Only a few cars remained in the parking lot. The rain had already stopped. The sun was still shining.

Cornell stepped out of his motor home. He walked to the front door and then walked inside. He didn't even wipe his wet sneakers on the mat.

To the right was the school office with a sign: "Please excuse our remodeling."

Wooden ladders leaned against the walls and stood in the middle of the hallway.

Old sheets covered things he couldn't see.

He saw stacks and stacks and stacks of fresh lumber, maple wood, he deduced from its color and grain.

He saw patches of fresh olive green paint covering the old dingy olive green paint.

Pieces of the floor were missing, where the old dull brown mastic tile was being replaced with new dull brown mastic tile.

The heavy air smelled of paint and tile glue.

Cornell turned to the office and knocked on the old maple door.

"Come in," a voice called out.

Cornell turned the creaky knob and stepped inside. The receptionist's office was empty of people. But it was full of cheerful, full pf green cacti, purple orchids, and delicate white ginseng. A door to his left was closed. The metal plate said, "School Secretary."

But the inner office door was open, and the light was on.

The man at the desk looked up. He had a square face, smiling eyes, crooked teeth, and thinning hair. He also wore an expensive suit.

Now Cornell didn't wear suits. Cornell only knew the principal's suit was expensive because he paid attention to the clues: the cashmere cloth, the gold thread in the handmade buttonholes, the sparkling diamond buttons.

Cornell wore faded and patched blue jeans, a light blue T-shirt stretched over his barreled chest, and his colorful patchwork blazer over that. His T-shirt read, "Eat, drink, and be scary." His curly black hair looked as if he hadn't combed it in days – which he hadn't. Because Cornell was too busy solving supernatural mysteries.

"Are you the principal?" Cornell called.

"Yes," Mr. Principal stood. "Are you Cornell Dyer?"

"Professor Cornell Dyer," Cornell corrected.

24

"Ah, yes. Professor. Please come in."

Cornell noted dingy walls, faded green cushions, and faded paisley carpet.

He noted nicked arms and legs on the maple wood chair, the nicked maple wood of the principal's desk, and the nicked maple wood of the many picture frames.

"Forgive our mess," Mr. Principal smiled and set a book over his papers. "We're remodeling our school."

Cornell sat on the chair and the springs squeaked. "Tell me about the job."

Mr. Principal sat and folded his hands. "We need you to teach science until the science teacher returns."

"What should I teach?" Cornell asked.

"Whatever you like," Mr. Principal said. "As long as it's science."

"For how long?"

Mr. Principal picked up a rubber band and rolled it between his fingers. "Until she returns."

"And you'll pay lots of money until she returns?"

"Of course, Professor. We pay all of our staff extremely well. We have an assistant principal, a receptionist, a secretary, a nurse, a cafeteria manager, three lunchroom workers, and homeroom teachers for all twelve grades, and teachers for all the subjects. We spare no expense when it comes to educating our two hundred and thirty-two students. In fact, every student gets twelve years of piano lessons and his or her own private piano."

"Can I see the classroom?"

"Of course, Professor." Mr. Principal stood and held out his hand. "The classroom is on the second floor, second door to the left."

Cornell shook Mr. Principal's hand.

Mr. Principal led Cornell to the hall. "Thank you again for helping us out."

"Sure," Cornell said.

Mr. Principal went back inside the office. Cornell heard the door lock.

Very strange, Cornell thought as he walked down the hall.

Old, dented metal lockers lined the halls. He saw an old-fashioned gymnasium to his left and a new-fashioned indoor swimming pool to his right. He heard the clang of old pipes and the hum of the central air conditioning.

He reached the stairs. He looked out the window. He saw a large running track, large basketball courts, large tennis courts, a large football field, a large baseball field, and an eighteen-hole golf course.

Cornell climbed the old wooden steps to the second floor. His footsteps echoed loudly in the nearly empty school. As he reached the second floor, a door flew open, and a man's head poked out.

The clean-shaven man wore thick glasses, a yellow cardigan, and a wide orange bowtie. His shiny black hair was slicked back with Billo-Cream.

"Oh, I'm sorry," the man said with a wide smile. "I didn't see you."

"Who are you?" Cornell asked.

"I am the history teacher," Mr. History Teacher said. "And who are you?"

"I am Professor Cornell Dyer. I will be teaching science here for…"

"Well, I must get going." He switched off the light and shut the door. "Enjoy your tour."

Mr. History Teacher started for the stairs. Then he stopped. Then he turned around. He smiled again, waved, and said in a Peter Lorre voice, "Gooood niiight."

And then he was gone.

Cornell continued to the science classroom. But he felt as if someone were watching him.

Being a supernatural super sleuth, Cornell was right. He just didn't know it.

For Cornell did not see another classroom door silently opening. He did not see a teacher poke his head out. He did not see the eyes of this teacher meet the eyes of Mr. History Teacher, who peered around the corner. He did not see them nod to each other.

Finally, Cornell reached the science classroom. He jiggled

26

the doorknob. The room was locked. So he peered through the glass window into the dark room.

Every desk and chair lined up with the seams of the tile.

The overhead projector stood on its stand, ready for the next day's classes.

A ring dangled from a short string of the rolled up wall map.

The chalkboard was wiped clean. The eraser was in the chalkboard tray and the pieces of chalk rested next to it.

An old skeleton hung from a pole in the front corner of the room, next to the windows. As Cornell's gaze wandered to the window shades, he felt the skeleton's eyes look at him – so Cornell looked back.

Actually, the skeleton didn't have any eyes, just eye sockets. But they were watching Cornell.

Cornell rubbed his own eyes. He must be sleepy. Or hungry. That is why his eyes were playing tricks.

Except the skeleton didn't want him to go. Cornell could feel it in his own bones. He saw it in the commanding eye sockets and steady gaze.

So Cornell stared back. Maybe the skeleton wanted to tell him something.

As a supernatural super sleuth experienced in solving supernatural mysteries, skeletons often talked to Cornell. But if this skeleton had a message, Cornell wished it would hurry up and talk. It was past his dinnertime.

But the skeleton did not speak, at least not with words. Cornell felt as if the skeleton had grasped his mind with its bony clawed hands and was pressing the words into his brain.

Cornell rubbed his eyes again. The skeleton's hands hung by its side. So Cornell hurried down the hall, down the stairs, and out the door. He couldn't wait to heat up a big can of beef stew. He couldn't wait to listen to his favorite Wagnerian opera. He couldn't wait to get a good night's rest.

But Cornell found an envelope tucked underneath his windshield wiper.

Inside the envelope was a note and a key to the Milton

Hotel.

The note said, "Your stay is on us. Thank you for helping us out." From the school board at Sunnystorm School.

FOUR-PLY VAMPIRE

By Sue Mydliak

I'd never given much thought to dying- though I'd had my reason enough in the last few months- but even if I had, I wouldn't have imagined it like this. Then, on top of it all, I survived. I wish I had died. The yearning, the need, the want of the one thing that will sustain my life is becoming extinct. Its texture, soft, sometimes course, but nevertheless, I crave it so much that I have dreams about piles and piles of it. Mountains of it. Such joy it gives my heart and then I wake up to my nightmare.

I stared across the long room, into the dark eyes of the hunter, and she looked pleasantly back at me. She's beautiful. Skin ivory, soft, scented lightly with Jasmine I just want to taste her lips. At least it was a good way to die.

I knew that if I'd never gone to China, I wouldn't be about to die now. But, terrified as I was, I couldn't bring myself to regret the decision. When life offers you a dream so far beyond any of your expectations, it's not reasonable to grieve when it comes to an end.

The hunter smiled in a friendly way as she sauntered forward to kill me.

****

Here I sit, half mad with hysteria, with towers of toilet paper rolls around me. Yes, that's right, I bought out the store. No one…I mean, no one will get what my body craves…toilet paper. Its thinness, texture and light scent drive me crazy. It
was that lady in China, she did this to me. Made me a vampire of the toilet industry. Now, with this Corona virus people are hoarding everything! They all think they're going to die, so what do they buy? My toilet paper!

I was out one night. I needed my fix. Four ply was my need this time. It's thickness. Chewing the papery texture, having it stick to the roof of my mouth…Oh, Lord I had to have it! All of it, but it would be a battle of wits.

As I made my way to the paper aisle I could see the baskets. There were at least five of them and loaded with…my toilet paper.

"No!" I screamed and ran at the ladies. You should have seen their shocked faces as I rushed their baskets and began biting into the fleshy, plastic wrap that held them together.

I was a madman for sure, but I didn't care. I bit into the first roll like a monkey on a cupcake. Oh, it was pure heaven. I couldn't stop. On and on I went till I saw a fresh roll and started in on it! The crowd grew around us. No one dared to come at me. There I was a roll in each hand and taking bites out of them both as if it were my last day. Tissue was everywhere. I even scraped up the bits that fell on the floor. Every morsel was tended to with such delight.

Then…

"Grab him!" They got me. I put up a big fight though.

With a muffled voice I yelled out as best as I could, "You'll neffer gef thefs tiffoos! Neffer!"

They locked me up. Fools. Don't they know you can't hold a vampire?

As I looked out my window, through the towers of my life sustaining source, I tried to remember what my life used to be like, as a human. Steak, potatoes, Sushi, fish and scores of other foods I'd eat and did I miss that? No. I mean, you don't need to grow toilet paper. You don't need to kill cows, pigs or goats for that matter. Toilet paper comes from trees. My brain started to reel. My mouth began to drool. I found a new food source. TREES!

HARD TIMES

By Tom Hernandez

War -- Civil and Cold and World (both one and two)
Red ribboned black flesh
chained to trees
Spirits destroyed one step at a time
Along a never-ending trail of tears
A legacy of land stolen by
Loud guns and quiet disease
Death by religion
Begging a deaf god
Hiding in ghettos, unknown to all
but the gas
Ash-covered souls rising through the chimney
Accepting a bullet in trade for freedom
Long promised, hard earned
Only to wait
And wait,
And wait
Listening to Crow songs for another 100 years
Vomiting from the smell of Strange Fruit
Sex, the only currency of real value
Taken at the end of a fist
Purple bruises the lasting receipt
Nail-pierced skin
Bones smashed
For daring to proclaim peace
For trying to break through walls
For putting heaven at our fingertips
And love in our hearts
A want-to-be king
Who blames the wood he cut
The kindling he laid
The gas he poured

The match he struck
For the flames consuming the castle
But if you think that was bad,
Oh my Gawd!
Try having to wear a thin, cloth mask

I REMEMBER

By Diana Estell

I remember the innocence when a heart didn't bleed. When time offered healing from wounds hours deep. Are memories meant to be remembered or buried in scars? Are they too deep to move, so deep in pain? Maybe memories can be winged or scythed in shame.

I remember the impurity when a black heart bleeds. When time offered brokenness from wounds years deep. Are memories nothing but lies over truth? Maybe memories are not winged or scythed in shame, for the hopeless have no refuge, no comfort to gain.

I remember the mending when a heart pumped red. When time offered hope from centuries deep. Are memories the answer to rise anew? Maybe memories are winged with eternal care. Angels pushed back the specter griping the scythe, to free my soul, to give me new life. I never want to forget who I was or where I came from, for my scars are my voice.

In my scars, I am free.
Free to remember
But no more a prisoner to.

IMANI IS HER NAME

By James Moore

Moses La Femme
hearkens to a voice;
let my people go
under cover of brush
sheltered by the night hues
carried by the wind
enslaved souls freed from bondage
someone holds her hand
someone holds her heart
Imani is her name
a self-taught man
soil, seed, strength
his only tools
the fruit thereof
frees minds and lives
of poverty's chains
a people risen from the ground up
her words intone
"you can build up a people with bricks and mortar"
Imani is her name
a spirited matron
tired from her toils
rest, respect all that she ask
indignity assigned to her from birth
despise validated by decree
humanity dismissed by custom
born a movement to strip Sheriff Jim Crow of his badge
she keeps our heroine still
she gives our lady hope
Imani is her name
a modern-day army,
diverse in its ranks

34

united in its cause
forged to battle
invasion of life
hopes and aspirations
they confront threats to the future
she resolves ambivalent hearts
and encourages war weary spirits
Imani is her name
hope amidst despair
bold among terror
guide through unchartered paths
Imani is her name
daughter of creation
sister of love
mother of vision
Imani is her name

IN DARK DEPTHS LURKING

By Denise M. Baran-Unland

Sue and Sam Barnes have just opened a diner in Munsonville, a depressed fishing village in Northern Michigan where all industry has nearly stopped. Sue has worked in the kitchen of Munsonville Inn all of her life and constantly hears singing. Sam is physically disabled. Neither know each other well or have business experience in this excerpt from "Call of the Siren."

As Sue had feared and Sam had hoped, the opening of Sue's Diner effectively shut down the kitchen at Munsonville Inn, and it didn't take long – just six months.

Villagers packed into Sue's Diner on opening day – October 29, 1926 – but only to Sue's amazement, for Sam never once doubted the villagers' loyalty to Sue and her food. They stopped patronizing the inn, and guests to the fishing village followed their lead. The dining room at Munsonville Inn simply became a lobby for the tourists the village typically attracted: the rich seeking a fishing or extramarital getaway and, occasionally, a few still hoping to catch a glimpse of the world famous John Simons, who was still packing concert halls around the world with his admirers, according to "the wire" stories in The Times.

Sue struggled to keep up with the orders, for, as Sue had predicted, Sam and his one good hand were little use in the kitchen. But he was outstanding at fraternizing with the customers and touting the food. Often when Sue swerved to see if the onions were sauteed, the sauce stirred, and the noodles boiled – small, but important tasks she relied on Sam to do – she only found an empty space where her husband once stood, along with charred onions, curdled milk, and mushy, nearly liquid, macaroni. Fuming, Sue would peek around the corner to find Sam hobbling about the dining room, greeting one and all as if he were Lord Barnes of Sue's Diner. Or, even worse, she'd see him perched on a counter stool with yet another cigarette and another cup of coffee, regaling his seatmate with another bad joke. Sue did the ordering, most of the putting away, the prepping, the cooking, the serving, the dishwashing, the cleaning, the bookkeeping. Fortunately, they had a tenant in the back upstairs apartment, the only reason they diner hadn't already failed. Unfortunately, the tenants themselves weren't stable. Mitchell Cooper had married a pregnant drifter named Ruth, who needed a last name for her baby and someone to support them.

"You – WHAT?" Sue had screeched when Sam broke the news, shortly after opening day.

"Shhh. Folks'll hear you clear to Evansville."

"I don't care if they hear me in Timbuktu! Tell them no!"

"Can't do that. Signed a contract."

Sue slammed her spoon onto the stove and thrust out her hand. "Give me the contract! Now!"

"Can't do that either."

"Why not?"

Sam grinned that crooked grin that used to turn Sue's belly to jelly.

"Why not?" Sue demanded again.

"I lost it."

She whipped the spoon at him. Sam ducked, and it hit the wall, leaving a splotch of grease as it clinked to the floor.

One day, Sue really had enough. After removing the offensive pots off the hot stove, she poured a cup of coffee, stomped into the dining room, helped herself to Sam's cigarettes and matches, and then plopped onto an empty counter stool. A customer at table fifteen, where Sam was gabbing away, noticed, and jerked his head in Sue's direction. The look of perplexed surprise on Sam's face was worth Sue's choking fit as she took her first drag of her first cigarette. Sam stumbled his way across the room as quickly as he could with a weak leg and cane. Fortunately, Sam couldn't move very quickly, which gave Sue more time to stop coughing and revel in his distress.

"What are you doing? Sam asked in a low voice once he reached the counter.

Sue blew out the smoke.

"Sue."

"Sam."

"Let's talk in the back."

"No."

"Everyone's staring."

"Don't care."

Sam snatched the cigarette from Sue; she flashed her middle finger as he snuffed it into the tray; he hobbled out the back door; the screen slammed with a bang, which made her start. Subdued, she scanned the room. Everyone *was* staring at her, with their mouths ajar or their forks frozen in mid-air. She slid off the stool and slunk into the kitchen. She washed her hands and donned a fresh apron. She put a kettle of water on the stove and chopped onions with a fury, wiping the tears off her nose with her sleeve, even though she knew better. What did it matter now? She imagined one hungry and impatient customer after another stomping out the door in search of better prospects. And it was all Sam's fault. Sam and his diner ideas! Why had she listened to him? Sue scraped the onions into a fry pan and dropped a great spoonful of butter on them, which sizzled on contact. Sue washed her hands, dried her hands, and reached for the flour, all the while cursing Sam. Soon, she was re-rolling the noodles, slicing them as thick as her finger, and dumping them into the boiling water, acts she once performed with an entire crew in the basement of Munsonville Inn, which Sam and his hair-brained ideas put out of business. Fresh anger flared as Sue stirred the browning onions and whisked butter and flour into a saucepan for the roux; slowly she poured milk into the mixture and blended the lumps away. She was basically a one-woman diner. She could not manage it all. After today, she probably wouldn't have to try. Because she most likely hadn't any customers anymore.

She heard the opening and closing sounds of the rear door, probably Sam returning for his cigarettes.

"Sue," a very familiar voice said.

Her heart stopped. She turned, stunned and with her eyes filling with tears. Nan, Dana, and Matilda were standing in the doorway with Sam behind them.

"We're here to work," Nan announced.

Sue moved the onions off the stove; she gently stirred the sauce.

"Sue?" Dana asked softly.

"Are you mad at us?" Matilda asked anxiously.

Sam eased around them. "Go talk to the customers. Find out what they need."

After they left, Sam put his arm around Sue, but she shrugged him off.

"Sue."

"Send them home, Sam!"

"I can't do that, Sue."

She slapped the whisk down and faced him, hands on her hips and her raging heart ready to rip out of her chest. "Oh, really! Then I'll do it!"

Sue started to push past him, but he held her back with his good hand.

"Sue, they want to help."

"No!"

"You're too late. I've already hired them."

"You idiot!"

"Keep your voice down! And don't call me an idiot!"

"You've hired them?"

"Yes!"

"Bryson Fox paid them almost twelve dollars a week!"

"So?"

"We can't pay that, Sam!"

"They agreed to work for less."

"Sam, we're barely turning a profit! We can't hire anyone!"

"We won't turn a profit if we don't!"

"If you'd look at the account books instead of playing Mr. Important out on the floor, you'd see this damn diner doesn't clear enough to pay anyone – including ourselves!"

"That's why they agreed to work for food, for now anyway."

"Are you lost your senses?"

"Have you lost yours?" He leaned his face close to Sue's; his eyes were blazing, and he spat out through gritted teeth, "We have PAYING customers upstairs and three experienced cooks who

39

WANT to work for free! And why is that? Because THEY see the vision in this place! That's more than I can say about the sniveling BITCH of an owner!"

Sam turned on his heel and angrily thumped out of the kitchen. Crying hard, Sue moved the saucepan off the stove and strained the noodles. She wanted to tear off her apron and storm out the door as easily as Sam had done an hour ago. But Sue didn't. Because Sue had people to feed. Sue had responsibilities that she took seriously, even if her drifter, no-name, running-away-from-an-evil-past husband didn't. Had Sam ever worked an honest day in his miserable, dishonest, rotten life?

"Probably not!" Sue shouted to the sauce.

But somehow, they did it. The five of them, while not pulling quite together, managed to serve anyone who came into the diner. They served them chicken, but they served it creatively. They cut and disjoined chicken after chicken. They basted the legs, thighs, breasts with melted butter and sweet herbs and baked them. They boiled the necks, backs, and wings, chopped them fine, and served them over biscuits with a cream sauce. They did the same with the giblets and served them over toast. Sue didn't see Sam the rest of the day; Matilda told her Sam was soothing rumpled feelings in the dining room with "some really amazing smooth talk." Sue ignored Matilda's admiration for Sam's "skills" and rapidly cut biscuit after biscuit after biscuit. No surprise that Sam was smooth-talking his way out it. Sam was a smooth talker. Sue knew that fact more than anyone. That's how he sealed the marriage deal with her. That's how he sealed the diner deal with the village. Bastard. No wonder why he got shot. If Sue had a gun, she'd shoot him herself.

Nan, Dana, and Matilda stayed until the last customer had finally left, the last crumb was swept, and the last light extinguished. Sue, anger cooled, walked them to the door, thanking them over and over for their help, while they hugged her and promised to see her very early tomorrow morning.

Sue locked the door and then leaned against it, suddenly overcome with exhaustion. But unlike regular people, Sue couldn't rest, not yet. She forced her tired legs to follow the stink of cheap tobacco to the table where Sam sat smoking in the dark, her mind running through all the possibilities for safe sleep tonight if Sam refused to come home or lock her in.

"I'm leaving," she hinted.

"Sit down."

She pulled a chair away from the table, its wooden, never-tired legs scraping loudly on the tile in the otherwise silent room. Her body sagged at the relief of sitting, and she stifled a yawn.

He picked up the case; it glinted in the light of glowing cherry. "Want one?"

"No."

He resumed smoking, holding the cigarette near his face between drags, and looking away from her. He looked tired. Yes, Sue was tired, but Sue was always tired after spending nearly seventeen hours on her feet. Her soles, and even her heels and toes, burned, and she felt nauseous from the feverish aching in her muscles that seven hours in bed didn't alleviate these days. Sam's tired was different, so different that Sue couldn't believe she hadn't noticed it sooner. His eyes didn't droop; they were dull. His face didn't sag; it was drained of all expression. Sam's tired couldn't be fixed with a long sleep because it was a tiredness of the spirit. It was the tired of one who had fought too hard and too long with too little results. Even Ma had more fire when she was dying. His saucy expressions and bold speech had masked this tiredness – until today, when Sue stripped them away. And she had no regrets.

Finally, Sam crushed the nub. He rubbed his weak hand clumsily over his face. Then he stood. So Sue rose, too. They walked out the front door, Sue first. He waited while Sue locked the door. They walked home, neither one speaking, while the night wind whispered across her face, her legs, and the hem of her dress, and raised the hair on her arms beneath her sweater; she squeezed and rubbed her hands to warm them, her eyes drawing to the sloshing lake as *the singing* sang on...

At home, Sue headed directly for the bedroom. She heard the familiar click. She stripped her clothes, carefully unfastened Sam's pearls and placed them in their little bag, selected a nightgown, and emptied her water before she climbed into bed,

41

pulled up her old Angel quilt, and groped under her pillow for words that always brought comfort. But Sue couldn't find any. So she let Wheeler decide. Sue riffled the pages and then stopped, letting her eyes fall to the poem fate chose for her.

"An Unfaithful Wife to her Husband"

Branded and blackened by my own misdeeds
I stand before you; not as one who pleads
For mercy or forgiveness, but as one,
After a wrong is done,
Who seeks the why and wherefore.
Go with me
Back to those early years of love, and see
Just where our paths diverged. You must recall
Your wild pursuit of me, outstripping all
Competitors and rivals, till at last
You bound me sure and fast
With vow and ring.
I was the central thing
In all the Universe for you just then.
Just then for me, there were no other men.
I cared
Only for tasks and pleasures that you shared.
Such happy, happy days. You wearied first.
I will not say you wearied, but a thirst
For conquest and achievement in man's realm
Left love's barque with no pilot at the helm.
The money madness, and the keen desire
To outstrip others, set your heart on fire.
Into the growing conflagration went
Romance and sentiment.
Abroad you were a man of parts and power--
Your double dower
Of brawn and brains gave you a leader's place;
At home you were dull, tired, and commonplace.
You housed me, fed me, clothed me; you were kind;

42

But oh, so blind, so blind.
You could not, would not, see my woman's need
Of small attentions; and you gave no heed
When I complained of loneliness; you said
"A man must think about his daily bread
And not waste time in empty social life--
He leaves that sort of duty to his wife
And pays her bills, and lets her have her way,
And feels she should be satisfied."
Each day
Our lives that had been one life at the start,
Farther and farther seemed to drift apart.
Dead was the old romance of man and maid.
Your talk was all of politics or trade.
Your work, your club, the mad pursuit of gold
Absorbed your thoughts. Your duty kiss fell cold
Upon my lips. Life lost its zest, its thrill,
Until
One fateful day when earth seemed very dull
It suddenly grew bright and beautiful.

I spoke a little, and he listened much;
There was attention in his eyes, and such
A note of comradeship in his low tone,
I felt no more alone.
There was a kindly interest in his air;
He spoke about the way I dressed my hair,
And praised the gown I wore.
It seemed a thousand, thousand years and more
Since I had been so noticed. Had mine ear
Been used to compliments year after year,
If I had heard you speak
As this man spoke, I had not been so weak.
The innocent beginning
Of all my sinning
Was just the woman's craving to be brought
Into the inner shrine of some man's thought.

You held me there, as sweetheart and as bride;
And then as wife, you left me far outside.
So far, so far, you could not hear me call;
You might, you should, have saved me from my fall.
I was not bad, just lonely, that was all.

A man should offer something to replace
The sweet adventure of the lover's chase
Which ends with marriage, Love's neglected laws
Pave pathways for the "Statutory Cause."

Sam lied.

Even now, Sue bristled at the memory of how casually he still shrugged off the truth, despite his fervent – and fairly regular – "slights of hand" that almost made Sue forget his lie in her many heated moments.

Still –

It was a semi-reluctant "still." But Sue had to grant Sam that "still."

Still, Sam was not the man in this poem; these words of Wheeler failed to stir her. Because Sam had never wildly pursued her, praised her dress or hair, or schemed to set her heart afire. Sam's deception was a deception of omission. He had a deal to seal, but he hadn't sealed her out, even though she was sealed inside the bedroom without him. For Sue dwelled in the "inner shrine" of Sam's mind. Even now, bereft of Sam's arms with only an Angel quilt to hold her close, even now on the other side of the locked door – mere feet away – Sue sensed her place in Sam's thoughts, even now, as he lay not sleeping, Sue knew he was thinking about her.

"I thought about you," Sam said earnestly. "I thought about you a lot. I thought about you doing this or doing that. Sometimes when I'd be doing – whatever – I'd think, "I wonder what Sue's doing now.' It lightened the load."

44

Sue recalled her heartache at Sam's public rejections. She recalled how quickly she married him for fear he'd run away, not fully understanding, until now, that Sam would never run away. She recalled how he pushed her to do more than she could while he did less than he ever had, and fresh anger flared like match to kindling. How dare he think that Sue could be chief cook and bottle washer, like Ma used to say? How dare he treat the diner as if it were a lucrative pastime when their survival was on the line?

But what Sue wasn't in this moment was afraid of losing Sam. She'd become one with Sam the moment she started living inside his thoughts, and, if he'd told the truth, that was long before he'd returned to Munsonville. She dwelled somewhere inside him the way *the singing* dwelled somewhere inside her. What did it matter how many "duty" kisses Sam might give her through the years – and, let's face it, most kisses were "duty kiss" now: the quick peck on the cheek or a light brush of his lips across her forehead. But Sam gave each of those duty kisses warmly, even if distractedly, and none left Sue standing outside in the lonely cold. So let the stormy tears fall, the winds of change blow; let her and Sam sweat under the heat of angry words or shiver with cold words best left unsaid. These things did not matter for she was in Sam's mind. She laughed at the church's notion that a marriage was not a marriage without, well, well, without the part Sam couldn't do. She thought of her and Luther with their eyes tightly shut against the other's body because others were in their minds. And yet, she was closest to Luther when she was in his mind, when he decided to answer her questions about the past even though it drudged up painful memories for him, when he bought a car to take her on a fact-finding mission to Jenson and Shelby, when he made a choice to sleep in her parlor for more than a dozen years to keep her safe. She thought of Sam tapping his way into Munsonville Inn every mid-morning to order breakfast, insisting only Sue could serve him. She thought of him leisurely smoking while leisurely reading through The Munsonville Times until the lunch rush was past. She thought of Sam happily enjoying the leftovers Sue served him. She thought of his grumbling: "I feel like a fucking lap dog. A useless, fucking lap dog."

Wheeler, as the neglected wife, had written:

Our lives that had been one life at the start,
Farther and farther seemed to drift apart.

But if Sue were writing the poem about her and Sam, the words might read:

Our lives that had been two lives at the start
Are one all day long; we're never apart.

Sue recalled her long days in the basement of Munsonville Inn without Sam. She recalled his insistence Sue start a diner they'd work together. How could Sue have been so stupidly blind?

"I love you, Sam!" Sue called out, realizing the moment the words left her lips she'd never uttered them to him aloud, ever. And Sam had only said those words once to her.

"Look, I love you!"
"Ha!"
"And you love me!"
"Not anymore!"

Sam didn't respond. But Sue knew he'd heard her.
She rolled onto her side.
The singing sang on.

"Hey, did you hear?" Dickie Elbert said early one morning as he set his copy of The Munsonville Times on the counter. "It's all over the radio, too."

Sue glanced down at the headline: *Stocks Crash, Wall Street Panics*. Sam snatched up the paper and quickly scanned the story. She didn't like the worry in his eyes when he slowly sat The Times back on the counter and tapped back into the kitchen, so she sped after him.

"Sam, what does it mean?" Sue asked breathlessly once they were out of the customers' hearing.

46

But Sam was counting cans of vegetables and motioned for her silence. He jotted the number on a piece of paper and then looked at her. "It means we're safe."

"Don't play with me."

"I'm not. We're safe, you and me, in Sue's Diner, where we don't keep our money in a bank."

"But you're worried." Sue accused, pointing her finger at him, and cutting him off with a flourish when he opened his mouth to respond, "Don't lie to me, Sam."

Sam looked away a moment, thinking. Then he leaned against the prep table and faced her, visibly troubled.

"Sam?"

"We are safe, Sue. But others are not. This may affect Munsonville."

"How?"

"I don't know. We might pay more for supplies. Customers might tighten their belts. The few businesses here might struggle – or fail."

"But we're safe – you and I?"

Sam nodded.

"Then why so glum?"

Sam didn't answer, so Sue walked over to him, placed a hand on each cheek and brought his face down close to hers. She didn't like the lost look in his eyes, so unlike Sam's almost annoying cockiness.

"Sam?"

He gently peeled her hands off with his good hand and returned his attention to the stock in the cabinets.

"I like the 'sameness' about Munsonville," he said. "I like it's predictability, it's dependability. I don't want that to change."

LITTLE BLACK BOOK OF PASSWORDS

By Steven James Cordin

I looked at the little black book and then at the dead man tied to the chair. "You should have waited till I got here to question him."

Maxwell shrugged. His mouth sounded full of wet gravel. "Yeah, well I didn't realize how fragile he was."

"He was seventy-five years old."

The short, stocky man sighed. "I always heard he was a tough old bird."

"Not that tough, apparently." I turned to Adams and tossed the little black book onto the kitchen table in front of him. "Did you figure anything out?"

Adams didn't look up from the old man's laptop on the table. A small black man, thin and wiry, his bald head gleamed under the kitchen lights. "Yeah, Jack. I figured out the code he used in the book. Simple. The old man skimmed about two hundred thousand over the last few years. Dates, amounts, and deposits. It's all here."

Maxwell whistled. "Why didn't he track it on the laptop instead of the book?"

Adams still didn't look up, a bloodhound on the trail for money. "He kept a phony set of records on the computer to show the boss. He must have kept the information on what he stole in the book in case the boss ever wanted to see the laptop."

"Okay." I walked over to the sink for a glass of water. "So, where is the money?"

Adams frowned. "I don't know. On the last page are a bunch of websites, User ID's and passwords. Four of these sites are for banks. I am guessing he opened accounts in all these banks and dumped the money in them. But I can't sign in using the passwords."

"Why so many banks?" Maxwell asked.

"Banks must report transactions that look suspicious or over ten grand to the Feds. He used several banks to hide the money." I shook my head. "And you killed him before we could figure out how to get the money."

"We weren't sure it was him skimming off the top when we got here." Maxwell grumbled.

I let it go. "Whatever. Adams, keep working on the laptop. Maxwell, go search the bedrooms for anything that might help find the money. I will search the living room."

I texted Fat Sam to take care of the body before I started searching, the man we called to dispose of bodies. Fat Sam owned a funeral home and crematorium. The old man, Trejo, would be a pile of ash in a few hours. Pity. Trejo laundered money for the boss for over fifteen years through his Mexican connections. Hard to believe he skimmed off the top. Laundering all that money for the boss finally got to him.

It didn't take us long to search Trejo's small two-bedroom house. We didn't find the money of course or anything to help us access the accounts. I plopped down on a chair next to Adams. He still pounded away at the laptop's keyboard. "No luck?"

He pushed the laptop aside and sat back in his chair. "Shit! I can't access any of these banks. These passwords just don't work!"

I took the black book and opened it to the last page. A list of websites and passwords covered the page in the old man's tight script. "None of them?"

"No."

I pulled the laptop over to me and stared at the desktop screen. The background showed a flag with green, white, and red vertical stripes. A large eagle, clutching a snake in its sharp beak, sat in the center of the white stripe. "What flag is this?"

"Mexico."

I sat back and thought. I looked around the kitchen, noticing a few Hispanic decorations, It began to click.

My eyes fell on Trejo's dead body, still tied to the chair.

Fat Sam should have been here by now. I called him on my cellphone.

Fat Sam picked up on the second ring. "Yo."

"Where are you?"

"What do you mean?"

"I thought you would have been here by now to get Trejo's body."

"Paulo called. He said to hold up and wait till he called back."

What? Paulo ran a crew on the east side of town for the boss. Not my favorite member of the team. How did he find out we braced Trejo and killed him? I hung up and turned to Adams. "Did you call Paulo and tell him about Trejo?"

"No."

I stood up and pulled out my piece. "Where is Maxwell?"

Adams stared at my gun. "I think he went into the bathroom."

I walked quietly down the hall. The bathroom door stood slightly ajar and through the crack I could see Maxwell. He stared into the mirror above the vanity, a gun in his hand. Shit. I crossed the space in front of the door hoping he wouldn't see me, then pressed against the wall. Adams stood at the other end of the hall. Without making a sound, I mouthed the words, "Call Maxwell."

Adams looked at me and then retreated out of sight. My heart began to beat faster. The little bastard bailed, but then his voice echoed down the hall. "Maxwell, can you come out here?"

The bathroom door opened, Maxwell started towards the kitchen, his back to me. I aimed my gun at his head. "What you call Paulo for?"

Maxwell stopped but didn't turn around. His gun pointed at the floor. "Why do you think, Jack? Two hundred thousand dollars, man."

"Put the gun down."

Maxwell still didn't move. "I don't think you have the nerve."

"Don't try me."

He did though. He started to turn, bringing the gun up. My gun barked its disapproval. Most of Maxwell fell to the ground. The rest splattered on the wall.

"Damn." Adams came back to the end of the hall. He stared down at Maxwell. "What is going on, Jack?"

I ignored him as I knelt to pick up Maxwell's gun. Maxwell's cellphone rang. I rolled him over to get at it in his jacket. I answered on the third ring.

"We are downstairs." Paulo's silky voice could make a veteran call girl quiver. He should have been a pimp. "Did you take care of them?"

"Sorry, Paulo. He didn't." I tried to sound cheerful.

Silence on the other end, and then Paulo hissed my name. "Jack. I should have known Maxwell couldn't get the job done."

"What the hell, Paulo?"

"What can I say? Its two hundred grand, and you are going to give it to the boss."

"It's his money."

"Doesn't have to be," Paulo replied, his voice smooth as a shot of Chivas Regal. "I'm coming in Taylor. We can cut a deal. Or you can die, Jack."

I hung up. Paulo would sink his fangs into me at the first chance. I looked over at Adams. His hands trembled. "You packing?"

Without a word, Adams pulled out his gun with a shaky hand. I thought he might shoot himself by accident. Adams was always shit at the strongarm end of things. "Go get behind the couch and when I signal you, just open fire on them."

He did as told. Could I trust him to shoot Paulo? I didn't know. I grabbed the chair with Trejo's corpse. His head lolled as I dragged him across the kitchen and into the doorway to the front room. I loosened one of his hands from the ropes and stuck Maxwell's gun in it. I found the light switch and smiled. A dimmer switch. The lights faded until I could only see a vague form in the kitchen doorway, a small gleam of gun metal resting on his lap. I crossed the living room to the bedroom hallway, stopping to scoop up the TV remote on the coffee table.

I pressed my back to the wall again. Someone pounded on the front door, muffled angry voices followed. The door burst open, but no one came through. Several shots rang out. Trejo's body jerked about with the impact of bullets and fell over. Maxwell's gun clattered to the floor.

Quiet filled the room. Slowly, a hulking figure, crouching low, breached the entry. Taylor. I hit the power on the TV remote, praying Adams knew what to do. The TV blared into life, its screen bathing the living room in dim light. Taylor pivoted and fired twice; the TV popped and fizzled out. Adams peeked up from behind the couch and fired. Taylor grunted. His dead weight fell to the floor. Adams stood wide eyed for a moment in the gloom. Never shot anyone before. Two more shots rang out, and Adams dropped behind the couch. I kept my place against the wall, trying not to breathe or make noise.

"You still alive there, Jack?" Paulo's smooth voice cut through the silence. "That was a good one with the TV. You always have a trick up your sleeve. But I see you laying there, and Adams is gone. It's over. You should have listened to my deal."

Paulo stepped into the doorway and fired twice, making Trejo's prone body twitch. Paulo ran his hand along the wall until he felt the light switch. As the lights came up, he confidently strolled into the living room, grinning. He frowned when he saw he shot Trejo.

"I always have more than one trick up my sleeve, Paulo." My gun barked one more time.

I checked on Adams. Dead. His loss. I went back into the kitchen, grabbed the black book and the laptop. I fled into the night.

I got to my car without any trouble. I didn't think anyone else came with Paulo. You could only split two hundred grand so many ways. I pulled out my cellphone, called the boss, and explained what happened.

The boss gave a few instructions. He didn't comment on Trejo's or Paulo's betrayal. Before he hung up, he added, "I will make a few calls. The police will not respond to any reports of gunshots. Good job, Jack."

At home, I turned on the laptop and pulled up the First National Bank website, one of the banks in Trejo's book. I studied the password on the last page of the little black book, "redmen1234." I typed "hombresderojo1234" into the password field on the login screen. I grinned as Trejo's account information appeared, showing a balance of forty-four thousand dollars.

I accessed the other accounts without a hitch once I found an English/Spanish dictionary. I transferred the money to the boss's account and mine. The boss already agreed to give me a third of what I recovered.

I called Fat Sam. "Hey, I've got a pick-up for you. Make that four."

JESUS IN OUR HEARTS

By Sharon Houk

Jesus in our hearts. Forever.

That's what Steven always said after grace, "Jesus in our hearts." And then me and Mom had to answer, "Forever." This was from when he was in the seminary in Charleston. It was never enough for him to just say grace. Same sort of thing with the grey and white cat that lived between the garages in the alley – he couldn't just put out a saucer of milk. It had to be tuna.

If Mom noticed a missing can of tuna, she'd go off, "The cat! The cat! What's with you and the cat?"

And Steven would holler from the backyard, "It's a child of God!"

Then she'd yell through the screen door, "I'm a child of God! You're a child of God! The cat is not a child of God!" And then to me in the kitchen she'd go, "I will kill that damn child of God if it takes any more of my tuna."

Steven got sent home from seminary for praying in the seminary grotto in his pajamas – in the middle of a snowy night with no shoes on. And for climbing the clock tower on a dare. And for being late to class on rainy days because he was picking earth worms out of puddles to save them from drowning.

Monsignor Stoffe put a one-word letter in Steven's file: "Unfit."

Then a month later Steven says to me, "I've joined the Marines." And off he went to Afghanistan. He was a pied piper and fed all the stray dogs outside of Bagram. He wrote that they were children of God. The dogs.

He was supposed to come back in 2017, but he got himself blown up by an IED. It hadn't been enough for him to be outside the wire. He had to walk point. Now Mom feeds a new stray cat tuna every day. She calls the cat "Jesus in our hearts." I don't. I call it "Forever."

54

LOSS

By Duanne Walton

It was expected.
It was unexpected.
It was a relief.
It was a shock.
It was welcomed.
It was unwelcome.
I gave God the glory.
I cursed the devil.
I waited for it to happen.
I got caught off guard.
All was right.
All was wrong.
Order maintained.
Chaos reigned.
Spiritual serenity.
Existential angst.
He passed on.
It was gone.
He still lives.
They're closed.
He's not gone.
They are gone.
He was my friend.
They were a routine.
He gave encouragement.
They brought stability.
Good company.
Good pizza.
Helpful friend.
Helpful employees.
I was his friend.
I was their customer.
He helped feed my soul.

They helped feed my body.
I'll see him again.
I'll never go back there again.
Peace prevailed.
Anxiety attacked.
All was right with the universe.
All was wrong with the universe - briefly.
New friends.
New pizza place.
Rest in peace, Rich Galli.
Farewell, Marcos Pizza.
Richard L. Galli
1939-2021
"Jesus said to her, "I am the resurrection and the life; the one who believes in Me will live, even if he dies, and everyone who lives and believes in Me will never die. Do you believe this?"
John 11: 25-26

I can't even imagine the pain one feels after losing a spouse. Recently a close family member has to experience this. In a vulnerable moment he conveyed a small glimpse of what he was and is feeling, and it touched me. It made me wonder what that could possibly be like, to be in his place right now. And thus - I wrote this fictional portrayal of what a day in his life right now, might feel like. Side note: Please cherish those you love, for we just don't realize how one moment can truly be the last.

LOSS

By Holly Coop

Beautiful fresh cut flowers, adorn a pearl white vase perfectly situated on an antique entryway tabletop. The colorful array of blooms mirrors those that also adorn the garden just outside the quaint, charming side porch of this house with a country flair.

The vase, in and of itself, is a testament of beauty with golden embellishments winding around the pearly hew of its body. Its breathtaking beauty is a hint of its class and elegance. A family heirloom, passed down from generations but never finding its truest beauty until placed in the hands of - my wife.

The house is empty and as I enter and close the door behind me I am consumed by the deafening silence. I glance at the vase, which looks exactly as it did when I left the house less than a week ago. The blooms appear fresh despite the air of death that now lingers.

I glance towards the staircase across from the entrance and my eyes are drawn upwards to the landing atop the stairs and to the rail just outside of our bedroom at the top of the stairs. My mind wanders to memories. I am consumed with memories. How can a simple staircase, how can looking up at a landing spark so many memories fusing through my exhausted mind?

I realize it's because I am not looking at just a staircase, or just a landing. I am reliving a staircase lined with holly berry garland and sparkling lights and grandchildren making their way down those stairs with anticipation and excitement on their faces - wondering what Santa left under Grandpa and Grandma's Christmas tree.

My eyes well, as I gather strength. I set my hat on the sofa in the living room where I left her, less than a week ago. She was sick and I was headed to the hospital for surgery. A surgery I was not able to postpone any longer although I wanted to. I wanted to stay in that living room. I wanted to tend to my sick wife, my wife who, a month ago was cleaning up after her family, my wife, who cared for everyone with the attentiveness of a saint. So much so that she often ignored her own health concerns, her own personal needs.

I sit on the sofa and look towards the spot where year after year, she put on display for all of our enjoyment, the most spectacular Christmas tree one could imagine. More magical than Santa could have done himself, every ornament hung artfully and with so much love and devotion to her family and our traditions.

How can a week's worth of days hold the weight of a lifetime of sorrow? How can you wake one morning to joy and fullness and then wake to another day drowning in the deepest part of lonely you have ever experienced?

As I ponder this, with the heaviest heart that I could ever have thought would hang in my chest, I get up, walk past the staircase and enter the dining room - her dining room. She made that room the most special room of the house just with her elegant presence adorning it. Many hours she spent doing what she loved, singing. Her voice filled the room on the many days I walked past, back and forth going from the kitchen to the living room, out onto the porch just outside the den. Back and forth past the staircase, up the stairs, outside, downstairs, to and from work. Did I hear her then, when her voice was painting the walls of that room? Did I notice the smile on her face when she sat there with her grandkids and played? Did I appreciate the many meals she cooked, the holidays she hosted, the weddings and funerals she attended with me? Did I see her standing beside me during the most trying times of my life? Did I tell her enough I love you and I am so happy you are my wife?

She brought the beauty out in that vase by the entryway door. She made the staircase come alive with excited pitter-patter of children's toes, past the holly berry garland with tiny pinecones. She fostered traditions making magic unfold. She cared for her family, protecting like the feminine lioness she was. And she touched the hearts of so many with her friendship. There has not been a more devoted daughter, sister, mother, and wife.

My wife, YES, I did hear. I did see. I did appreciate and I will forever miss my love.

There has been loss. I have suffered the pain of losing many, many loved ones. But the empty I feel now is nothing I have ever known. The depths of this empty, is not contained by the description of words. There is no way to describe. How does one begin to tell the story of oneself, separating from one's life source? When you have lost your life long mate, you have lost the largest part of your own being. Your very own existence is threatened. How can half a heartbeat? How can half a soul feel joy, how can only memories fill my being with the energy needed to survive – after losing my wife?

I sit in the dining room, and in the deafening silence I hear not with my ears but only within my heart - my half a heart, the whisper of the Lord - you can do all things in Christ who strengthens...

Faith fills my half a heart with enough energy to carry on and I trust, will continue to sustain me until the time comes for me to once again be joined to my wife. When my heart will become whole again and my soul will be fully filled with joy.

Until then I will spend many hours walking through that entryway, admiring the lovely staircase, enjoying holiday decorating with family in the living room and sitting in this dining room where the essence of her soul remains. In the silence I can hear her precious voice bouncing off the walls. And though I am empty with loss, this house is forever filled with her song.

PARASOMINA

By Jennifer Russ

"You should get some sleep."

Aiden exhumed his face from the computer screen and met the saucer eyes of his boss' assistant, Sophy. Her round features molded from puppy dog tails and teddy bears inflicted a moment of disorientation within the sharp edges and muted the wall colors of the advertising office.

"You should stop telling people what to do. That's Ed's job, remember?"

Aiden returned to the hazy, backlit wall of text and flexed his claw over the number pad. Sophy shifted on her feet, chewed a thumbnail, and shot her next shot.

"I mean it. You look half dead, Aiden." She leaned in and whispered deviously. "You're scaring Sandra."

He met a pair of Coke-bottle glasses gaping from across the room and the nosey HR rep immediately took an interest in her 'Grandma's Have the Greenest Thumbs' mug. Aiden blinked, tuned it all out, and faced his office friend with a semi-convincing jest.

"Don't you have something to do? Doesn't Ed need coffee or a human sacrifice or a burrito from that stand that also sells umbrellas?"

Sophy, seemingly unoccupied, leaned upon his jutting desk and stared intently at his face. Her lips ticked up just enough to ease the mood, and one side of her thick curls escaped from the headband restraint.

"Ed took a personal day. He'll never know." She gave him Christmas morning eyes. "Go. I'll cover for you. Just take thirty. Have a nap and something decaffeinated."

Aiden squinted, rubbed at his cold cheeks, and glanced at the never-ending stack of paperwork. His body sagged at the implication, each muscle loosening just enough to give him a glimpse of his level of exhaustion. It'd been nearly a week since his last decent night of sleep, a week of bad infomercials and even worse

60

takeout. The pills didn't help, the supplements tasted like powdered puke, and the two hundred-dollar 'sleep light' only entertained his cat.

What the hell. A break couldn't hurt.

"Alright, you win. I'll take ten." He pushed back from his desk and glanced at the appealing neon 'exit' sign in the vacant hallway. "Thanks, Soph."

The bubbly girl smiled and then eased, as if his presence was enough to tie her in knots. He walked a straight line to the men's room, passing other hunched, zombified business suits and typing fists. He would have made it unnoticed if not for...

"Aiden!"

Aiden rubbed at the bridge of his nose, scratching an itch. "Yea, Jeff?"

"Hey, you hear about Ed?" The sasquatch of a salesman lumbered over as if they were long-lost friends. "Big Guy freaked out at lunch yesterday, yelled something about locusts in his triple espresso. Now he's out on a personal day. Yea, right." A five-by-seven piece of cardboard hit Aiden in the chest. "Your turn to sign the 'don't die' card."

"Uh, not right now. I have to, um...."

He faced the man head-on and watched his chiseled exasperation crumble.

"Whoa, you get into a fight?" He lowered his voice. "Next time, call me. I could use a good punch in the face. Works better than Nyquil, I hear."

Aiden frowned and glanced at the naked stickman on the swinging door to his left. "No, I just haven't been sleeping. I'm gonna..." He pointed to the bathroom.

"Yeah, sure." Jeff raised the card, disturbingly serious. "Hey, chip in a few bucks, too. We're getting an Edible Arrangement."

Aiden marched over the sticky tile and stopped at the streaky mirror. He leaned in and observed the bruises beneath his eyes. They expanded slightly further than the usual hollow borders of dark circles, even encroaching on his nose. He touched one, feeling no pain, and stretched the skin around until he could see into the pink beneath his eyeball.

The lights flickered, buzzed, enticed him with their brief darkness before regaining function.

"Huh, maybe I will take thirty."

Thirty turned into sixty, which turned into a personal day when Sandra startled at the sight of Aiden and dropped her coffee on his lap. He packed up his things, threw some papers into his briefcase, and trudged to the nearest subway stop. Passengers glanced at him and then quickly looked away with a wrinkle in their noses. He layered his raincoat and his bag atop the feces-brown stain on his crotch and watched his reflection darken in the window.

The train stalled two stops too soon and Aiden trudged the rest of the way.

At home, he removed his tie, dropped his pants into the laundry bin, and crawled onto the leather sofa. He flipped on a TV show about alien civilizations and told himself to sleep.

His eyes never closed, his lids frozen apart. Sounds lulled around him like gargantuan beasts lumbering in his peripheral. Something growled, maybe his stomach. He ignored it, the kitchen feeling like a three-day quest on rough terrain. He rubbed at the tingling sensation in his cheeks as the dramatic man with big hair spoke of time travel and black holes born of human hosts.

The insectoid alien fled the galaxy fifteen episodes later when the glare of sunlight and the deafening chorus of car horns dragged Aiden from the void between sleep and wake.

He buried his face in the pillow and moaned. "One the seventh day, he went to work."

Aiden slithered from the sofa, dragged clean fabric over his aching joints, and waited five minutes for an elevator that abruptly stalled halfway up. He used his last dregs of energy to maneuver the stairs and evade a herd of gaping children and their overprotective parents on the way to the nearest cab.

He did it all without a single glance in the mirror.

………..

Aiden cleared the doors of the office, his posture slumped, and halted when Sandra shrieked and made confetti of a stack of papers.

"What now?"

"Your face!"

He palmed at his cheeks, now numb to the touch, and scurried down the hallway to the men's room. Pushing past a couple of lingering sales guys, Aiden put his nose to the mirror and contorted his lips into a tangled grimace.

The dark circles had expanded down his nose and into the middle of his face. The varying shades of black and gray swirled together like soft serve and created an illusion of depth. He fingered the skin, cooler than the rest but still solid despite the apparent translucence, and traced the border of the darkness.

"What's happening to me?"

Three knocks. Aiden turned to meet Sophy's red curls peering through a crack in the door.

"Aiden, Sandra's freaking out. You're still not sleeping?" She took a hesitant step through the threshold and raised her hands. "Okay, don't panic. I can help."

"No, you can't." Aiden repelled from the mirror and paced back toward the stalls. "No one can help me. I'm going to be awake forever. Or until I lose my mind. That happens, right? I think I read that somewhere. This guy on the radio…"

Sophy raised her hand to silence his rant. "You know Gail, my girlfriend? She's a sonologist." He scrunched his eyebrows. She rolled her eyes and clarified. "She's a doctor at the sleep institute."

"Why didn't you say that the first time?"

"First of all, rude!" She stepped closer. "Second, she can help you."

Aiden squinted, his head swimming, and returned to the mirror to touch the growing bruises. His body felt like a barbel taking on more weight by the minute. It couldn't handle much more without breaking. What did he really have to lose?

"Okay, yeah. I'll try anything at this point."

The lights buzzed, went out, and surged back to life. A low, disturbing growl met Aiden's ear. He whined and grasped the cold porcelain sink with white knuckles. Sophy, her face sunken and now angled in determination, met his eyes in the mirror and presented a card.

"Here, this is her address." Aiden studied the plain black text and lipread 'Gail Peterson, MD.' "You should head over there right away. I'll call her and tell her it's an emergency."

Aiden hugged his friend in thanks, exchanged a brief smile. "A doctor, huh? Way to go."

She smacked his shoulder. "Shut up. Go fix your face."

They parted ways. The lights flickered. A voice boomed.

Hello Aiden.

He turned to find Sophy already gone, the bathroom empty, and the exit door swinging.

………..

Aiden managed to make it to the tenth floor of the medical office building before the elevator clunked, squealed, and gave way to darkness. The red emergency light popped on to reveal a blurred, mutated version of his face and blotches that expanded like magma after a volcanic eruption.

His fingers trailed down his temples to his freezing cheeks.

Then into them.

Aiden gasped, shivered, and immediately retracted the frosted digits. Ice held them together like Velcro, his skin burning with cold. He yelped and frantically flexed his fingers in a scissoring motion. The fifth try parted the icy red flesh, and it stretched until it painfully separated.

"This is a dream. It has to be a dream."

The elevator door chimed and opened, proving him wrong. Aiden brushed the ice from his raw fingers just as a heavyset middle-aged woman with a ginger ponytail and a white coat peered down from the heavens.

"Aiden, I presume? I'm Dr. Peterson. Gail to you." The red light, now blinking, must have shielded her from his appearance. Aiden raised his hood regardless and looked away when she spoke.

64

"I'm sorry about the elevator. It's never done this before. The maintenance men are working on it. Come on, let me help you to the office."

"Thank you." He took her offered hand, climbed onto the waist-high tile, and followed her through a maze of white lit with fluorescence. "I really appreciate you getting me in." Each bulb surged as they passed, and Aiden's cheeks grew colder.

"Of course, Sophy sounded worried."

We're here Aiden…

He circled around, searching for the owner of the creepy whisper, and returned to find Dr. Peterson gesturing into an open door. "Come in, please."

He entered a sterile sleep study room containing one queen-sized bed and countless reflective surfaces. Passing an interrogation mirror the size of a wall, Aiden sat on the bed and pulled his hood down as far as possible. The doctor dragged a chair up close and attempted to peer under his shield.

"Sophy mentioned that you've been having trouble sleeping. Can you tell me how that began?"

Aiden's skin crawled while he recounted the events of that night seven days ago.

"I had this nightmare. These hideous creatures crawled through a portal and took over the earth. They killed everyone, tore their skin off, used them as incubators. It was the end of everything. Look, I know this sounds ridiculous and I sound crazy, and maybe I am, but I can't close my eyes. It's like something is freezing them open from the inside."

Someone…

"Are you hearing voices, Aiden?"

He raised his hood and made eye contact for the first time. The doctor, to her credit, only slightly flinched.

"Knock me out. Stitch my eyes closed. I'll be fine if I can just get a few hours. Please."

Dr. Peterson snapped on some gloves. "Let me take a look at those bruises." Her rubber fingers grazed the silky skin around the malignance and then Aiden felt something move beneath his cheekbone.

The lights flickered. The doctor gasped. Slowly, she pushed her chair back, stood, and looked at him as if he were a bomb about to explode.

"It will be okay, Aiden. I just need to speak to my colleagues."

Aiden swallowed, nodded. "Yeah, okay."

She left, clicked the door closed behind, and Aiden's stomach sank. He considered running away, breaking the window, leaping to his death.

Come, Aiden. Come, say hello.

The voice, low and venomous, called from the mirror and tempted him forward. Defeated, exhausted, Aiden stood on legs no longer his own and slowly approached, afraid of the monster he'd find. The lights turned off and on again. What emerged was more of a wormhole than a face. Aiden moved his lips, tried to form words. Couldn't. He pressed his finger inside until it disappeared down to the nub.

Then a finger reached back.

He wheezed, screamed, and then stumbled backwards.

"Hey, help me!" He yanked his finger out and slapped his face repeatedly. "Something is here."

Aiden blinked and the saw that nightmarish wasteland behind his eyes. A locus-like beast, with scales for skin, towered over the rubble that once made up his city. Boney creatures with layers of eyes crawled from within the bodies of the survivors and left the flesh suits behind like dirty laundry. A face like a praying mantis with beady eyes and fangs stared out from within his mind, commanding it all.

"Whatever you are…" Aiden angrily sobbed, the salty drops never reaching his lips. "…get out of my face!"

When Aiden blinked again, the mirage disappeared. He caught his image in the reflective surface and froze. The swirling void now encompassed his entire face apart from his large, petrified eyes. A jagged, boney tentacle emerged from within his cheekbone and stretched his skin to reveal a single, blinking, crimson eye.

66

You should get some sleep, Aiden.

He choked, wheezed, gasped as the portal opened beneath his eyes to reveal the next dominant species.

Finally, Aiden slept.

SALT

By Colleen H. Robbins

She woke to a mouth full of cotton, scratchy red eyes, and a malaise that she just couldn't shake. The clock read 11:30, and the brightness of the sun warned Charlene she was coming down with a migraine. Great, another bad day. She called off work and opened her laptop, then googled her symptoms. Too many possibilities. She rubbed the sore spot on her neck. The swollen bite mark itched. Bastard gave me AIDS or something. Well, the fertility clinic wasn't going to help me anyway.

The coppery taste in her mouth revolted her, almost as bad as the peppermint of her toothpaste. She dropped her toothbrush in the sink when a car backfired outside her apartment. She was rinsing it off with shaky hands when a child shouted. Charlene fished it out of the toilet this time and threw it away.

An afternoon nap helped. She woke again after dark craving salt--another PMS day. She had too many of them. She dressed, applied some foundation, and headed out the door. Heels clicking, she made it halfway to Chin's Take Out when another car backfired and a wave of weakness sent her stumbling against a building. This is too fast, Charlene thought. AIDS doesn't kill this fast. She slid down in a growing puddle and finally understood that she had been shot.

#

"Welcome back." The voice rang with odd harmonics that she didn't recall ever noticing before. She lay full length on a steel table--it was steel, she could smell it--and listened to the drip of water in the next room. She must have imagined the voice; she did not hear any breathing.

"I know you are awake." The harmonics fascinated her.

Charlene opened her eyes. Bare pipes ran along a high-vaulted ceiling between the dull glare of fluorescent bulbs. A track light pointed off to one side.

She turned her head toward the voice. A pale young man wearing a stained white apron and blue surgical mask slouched against a second table. A tray of surgical instruments lay nearby.

He pulled off his gloves with a snap. "You're lucky tonight's my duty night. I saved your life." He snickered and then broke into a high-pitched giggle that ended with a donkey-like bray. She winced at the contrast with the harmonics.

"Yeah, well, thanks, Doctor." Charlene sat up.

He snicker-giggle-brayed again. "Not a doctor," he managed to get out. "Just Ed."

"Okay, just Ed. I'm better now so I'm going to leave." She slid off the table.

Ed stood between Charlene and the door before she saw him move. "You're not going anywhere until your sire shows up."

"Nope, sorry. No knights in shining armor for me. Hell, I can't even buy sperm at a fertility clinic. Now get out of my way before I hurt you."

That set him off on another snicker-giggle-bray. "You're funny, girl. The guy who made you. Who is he? I'll call him."

"My name is Charlene, not girl. And there is no guy who made me. I paid for college on my own, got my job on my own, and rose up through the ranks on my own merit. Nobody made me." She gave Ed a toothy grin. "You got anything salty around this place? I could kill for a pretzel right now."

He stood back and cocked his head to one side. "Um, you can't eat pretzels anymore."

"Why the hell not?" Charlene advanced on Ed, backing him into a corner. "Don't tell me I can't have salt anymore."

"Okay, how about I tell you you're a vampire. Forget the pretzels."

Charlene wavered on her feet, unable to speak. A what? This can't be happening. How will I ever have a baby now?

Ed edged past her and stood in the middle of the room, eyeing the door. "Didn't your sire tell you what would happen?"

"The bastard that attacked me on the street? He never said a word. Yeah, find him for me. I'll rip his heart out instead of just a piece of his arm." She snorted. "A vampire. I thought he gave me AIDS."

#

The vampire community was smaller than she expected. It looked just like every cocktail party she ever attended: the group got their drinks and broke up into cliques. Same large room, same artwork scattered about, just the outfits were older. She felt out of place in her silver midriff blouse and blue-striped skirt.

Ed handed her a cup of blood. He dressed better away from the morgue. Charlene swirled her drink as he introduced her to the first clique. One other woman stood across the room, a petite girl barely past puberty. Charlene took a sip of her drink. At one point she saw her sire across the room; he didn't appear to recognize her. Not too bad-looking for a vampire, either.

Charlene found a young-old vamp--he claimed twelve centuries but could have passed for seventeen years--and asked questions about vampire history. She was beginning to get used to the harmonics in vampire speech. Maybe after she spoke with a third vampire it would seem normal. After a while she looked around the room at the various cliques and their wine glasses of blood. "So where do you put all the baby vamps when the parents are out partying? Is that where all the women are?"

The chatter in the room stopped. "There are no baby vampires." She didn't see who spoke, but his voice sounded as flat as the tick from a failing metronome. No music at all.

"There were once." The young-old vampire's voice rang loud in the silence. "My sire was true-born."

"So what's the problem? Are you all impotent?" At Charlene's words, numerous voices protested. Most lacked the harmonics.

Charlene's sire crossed his arms. "The problem is with the females, not the males. Modern females are infertile." Such a flat voice.

The vampires nodded and agreed, then fell back to their small conversations.

Ed touched Charlene's shoulder. "You wouldn't want to be fertile around this group anyway. They're kind of medieval." Snicker-giggle-bray. "They'd keep you pregnant all the time."

She noticed the harmonics in his voice again. Only a few vampires in the room, including the young-old vampire, had the harmonics.

Being pregnant all the time didn't sound so bad to Charlene. She had always wanted a houseful of children. The voices around the room dropped to whispers, and she caught several vampires sneaking glances in her direction. She tugged at Ed's sleeve. "Let's get out of here."

They walked most of a mile before she spotted the basketball game in a street-lit lot. Drawn like a moth to a flame, she stood at the fence line and watched a particularly tall man in his twenties make basket after basket. Well built, athletic, he would make good babies. Better than any vampire would.

"I want him," she whispered. "How do I... um... can vampires hypnotize people?"

Ed smiled. "Hungry, huh? It takes a few months to learn how. I'll get him for you. Wait in the alley."

Charlene found a relatively clean spot and leaned against the wall. The tall man walked into the alley like a sleepwalker, slowly oriented on her, and approached. He sank to his knees and slowly turned his head to one side. She could smell the sweat running down his back.

"Get up. C'mon, stand up!" She didn't want to bite him. She wanted a baby from him. When he remained still, she loosened his belt and kissed him.

That got a response. He straightened his head. leaning into her kiss. A few seconds went by and he pushed her away, leaping to his feet.

"What are you, nuts?" His voice was a surprisingly high tenor. "This here's a Neighborhood Watch Zone. You go take your business somewhere else before I call the cops."

Charlene turned and fled as he pulled out his phone and started to dial.

Ed caught up with her two blocks later. "Good meal?"

"Meal? That's not what I wanted him for." She punched Ed in the shoulder. "He thought I was some kind of a streetwalker."

Ed doubled over as she punched him. His braying laugh followed Charlene down the street, mocking her.

#

"This one better work out." Charlene spooned pretzel salt into her mouth. The discarded box of frozen pretzels defrosted slowly on the kitchen counter. "The last one was gay, the one before that worked in an Italian restaurant--couldn't you smell the garlic on him?--and the first one thought I was a whore."

"Hey, I would have thought you were a whore, wearing that silver shirt in the alley." She threw the spoon at him. Ed ducked out of the way. "William's good. He has kids."

"Where are we meeting him?"

"That little diner on First Street. There's a motel around the corner."

"Okay, but this is your last chance. If this doesn't work, you have to teach me to hypnotize in like a month."

Ed groaned. "Let's go. He always gets there at eight o'clock for a cup of coffee."

Charlene headed straight for the pay phone when they reached the diner, then continued on into the bathroom when the phone had no receiver. She waited two minutes and returned to the main room. Ed stood at the counter with a middle-aged man wearing a black button down shirt. At his nod, the three of them left together.

Around the corner, Ed signed them into the motel and busied himself at the computer in the lobby. Charlene went upstairs with William. What little he said vibrated with some of the same harmonics.

They kissed--the worst kiss she could remember, but if it resulted in a baby it was worth it--and he started mechanically unbuttoning the black shirt. An intricately carved wooden cross hung around his neck on a fine gold chain. Charlene backed across the room as William reached for her. The cross brushed her arm as she ducked under his reach and ran out the hall door. William followed her down to the lobby.

72

He pursued her until an elderly matron touched his arm. "Father William, what are you doing?"

Ed ducked and ran. Charlene chased him all the way back to her apartment. He dodged around the kitchen table.

"I didn't know he was a priest! What's a priest doing with six kids?"

"I bet you're not Protestant, either. You idiot." She held up her arm. An angry scorch mark marred her pale flesh.

"Ouch. Hey, let me take care of that." He poured her a cup of blood and went into the bathroom for the first aid supplies. After he slathered her burn in antiseptic cream and wrapped it loosely in a bandage, Ed kissed her forehead.

He has such compelling eyes, she thought. He didn't look too bad, either. Not too muscular, not too thin. When he kissed at her cheek, she turned to meet his lips.

#

The only thing wrong with pregnancy is the cravings. Human blood just wasn't good enough. She and Ed had three children already, with a fourth due in a few more months. She enjoyed the attention the other vampires gave her, each trying to convince her to leave Ed and have a child with them. The infertile ones bugged her the most. She could tell now; just as she could from her first day as a vampire. It's the music in their voices.

The older infertile vampires were particularly tasty. Salty, almost. Besides, who would notice if an old vamp disappeared now and then?

The doorbell rang and Charlene answered it. Her sire stood there clutching a bouquet of roses. Only yellow blooms, but they would do. She invited him in and went to find a vase.

SINGING BOWLS FOR HEALING SOULS

By Holly Coop

Let the sound wash over you
Let its energy vibrate through you
From the top of your head to the tips of your toes
Wake up mind it's a new day
Fluttering eyes take in the beauty that surrounds

Inhale
The sweetness of being alive
Exhale
Any energy that binds

Heart beating in tune with Mother Earth
The universe sustaining
Every breath
A birth
Every exhale
A death

Ebbing and flowing
From ignorance to knowing
Seeing learning growing

Sounds vibrating
Waking your soul
Feel it glowing

Grounded
Ready
Embrace
The day
Let yourself BE
In its flow

SLEIGHT OF HAND

By Cean M. Magosky

Football practice ended late. After last Friday's game that was to be expected. I played tackle on the varsity and was seeing quite a bit of playing time for being only in my third year of high school. After a quick shower, I ran the ten blocks home where I knew Dad would be waiting, pacing back and forth and chewing on his cigar. Dad was a patient man and that was a good thing in his business, all the same I preferred to cause as little fuss as possible. That night was a special night and he had been working a long time to make it happen.

Dad was expecting Mr. and Mrs. Castelli. He had been trying to get the Italian business ever since prohibition started, everyone had. The Italians were a close-knit community buying only from other Italians. Even getting the Castelli's to talk with him was a big deal. Dad was known as 'Char the Irishman' though he had not a drop of Irish blood in him. He came from a long line of German stone cutters and casket builders. He married a fiery Irish woman and probably figured that if he had to put up with that temper, he had every right to call himself an Irishman. Dad was a large man, at least six-foot-six and three hundred pounds, who loved horses, cigars and derby hats, though not in that order. One time he had boasted of having the fastest horse in town, of course he also said that being a German Lutheran and courting an Irish Catholic girl, having a fast horse was a matter of necessity.

I had worked the last three nights on getting the order perfect. Dad had searched every warehouse for the correct labels and paid top dollar for them. There were enough for each bottle to have its own label. That was not always an easy trick in those days. Early on in prohibition, we could get labels cheap because everyone figured they were useless. The distributors practically gave them away. What they didn't realize, at least not at first, was that if you slap a high-class label on a bottle of grain alcohol, cut with a little water, the average man couldn't tell the difference. It was easy at first, like I said, we could get anything they wanted. If they asked for Hiram Walker, we got it. Jack Daniels, no problem. We even got a load of Canadian labels. That got us a real good price, almost double the going rate. Dad made up some story about sneaking it through the border in cases of bear steaks. I had a hard time keeping a straight face through that one. Then the distributors caught on and labels got scarce and expensive. At first, we cut back to labeling every other bottle, then every fifth. Occasionally a case went out with only one labeled bottle in the entire case. We had worked out a code where on the outside of the boxes were a series of numbers which indicated the location of the labeled bottles so that Dad could reach into the case, seemingly at random, and pull out a labeled bottle of the appropriate brand.

Anyway, I had just spent three nights pasting labels and filling bottles with alkie water and a little food coloring to make them look just right. I was up until at least midnight or one o'clock every night. Between high school, football practice, homework and packaging liquor, I barely had time to sleep. But it was how we paid the bills. When the amendment went through, Dad had to close the tavern. We had no choice. Besides we had all this booze just lying around. He started selling locally to friends and old customers. They all knew that a tavern owner must have something left over they could secure for a small under the table fee. As the business grew, we started making our own in the basement and headed to the smaller towns of central Illinois. Making liquor wasn't hard, all you needed was something to ferment and a place to ferment it. The basement of the old house where we lived was a maze of dark rooms and cubby holes, perfect for keeping a few secrets. Most of the deals were done by word of mouth, a friend of a friend, and the routine was always the same. Dad would park on the side of the building and go check the place out while I waited in the car. I was bigger than the average kid so I was capable of deterring most trouble makers. Dad would come out the front door and light his cigar, that meant the deal was done and I could haul in the cases from the trunk of the car. I would then wait while they inspected the merchandise and settled the bill.

The Italians were coming to the house. This had never been done before but Dad said he wanted to gain their trust. He said trust was the key, if they trust you, you've got 'em. I just shrugged my shoulders and continued pasting labels and packing cases.

When I got home, the Castelli's were already in the kitchen talking nervously with Dad. The scent of garlic mixed with the coffee and tobacco and potatoes to create a cloud that was almost overbearing. I stumbled to the kitchen, gasping for breath and trying to compose myself. I stood blocking the doorway taking in the scene. I had done enough lookout work to quickly assess the goings on. Mr. Castelli was a small man with silver hair and deep brown eyes. He wore an immaculately pressed but worn white shirt, open at the collar and brown trousers. The woman with him was short but ample. She had deep eyes similar to her husband's but with a bit of a glint in them. She wore a simple red dress with a black shawl around her shoulders and stood about a half step back and to the side of her husband clutching a worn black purse. They were standing across the table from my parents. My mother was wore a bright blue dress and starched white apron. Dad wore his usual dark grey suit and tie. His trademark derby sat on the table in front of him. It was never far away. He plucked the cigar from his mouth and introduced me.

"This here's my boy, Will. We have no secrets in this family, do you mind…" his voice trailed off. The little man shook his head. I offered my hand but the offer was not returned.

"Mister Char," Mr. Castelli began, his voice halting in broken English. "You know, my customers, they are very particular and we have a large wedding this week. They need much liquor and my regular friend cannot help me. This is why I come to you." Dad smiled around the cigar and blew out a cloud of smoke.

"Well, you're in luck. I just got a couple cases of some fine quality liquor, I think you'll be pleased." Dad nodded and I hurried down the basement steps to retrieve a bottle of red wine and a bottle of whiskey. I gave the wine bottle a spin to make sure the food coloring had not settled as I climbed the stairs. I placed the bottles on the table. "You may inspect them, shall we open one?" Dad motioned Mother to pass a glass. Mr. Castelli's face soured as he tasted the red liquor.

"It has been so long since I have tasted this good a wine that I fear I am not accustomed to anything so strong." I felt my face becoming warm, was he onto the trick? "I am sure that once I become once again accustomed to this fine wine it will be much better." Dad smiled at me, an easy smile that somehow didn't make me feel much better.

"So, I trust this will be suitable."

"Yes, this is very good. How much do you have?" Dad looked at me, chomping the cigar the whole time.

"How much do we have, son?" He winked as he asked the question in a dramatic fashion. Char was above all else, a showman.

"Well, Dad, I think we've got about four cases of the red and two of the whiskey." I tried to match his tone, which drew a scowl. He hated to be upstaged.

"Will that do, Mr. Castelli?" The aged Italian man looked at his wife who stuffed a hand into a patch pocket on the front of her dress and produced a worn handkerchief.

"That will be fine. I can help the boy load the car."

"No need for that, he's a young boy. Plays football, can probably use the exercise to make him stronger. Let's have a drink, since this bottle is open." I slipped back down the staircase to the basement and out the bulkhead doors. I loaded the cases into the trunk of Mr. Castelli's sedan then went back into the kitchen.

"All done," I said, flapping a bit of dust off my slacks. Dad and Mr. Castelli each held a glass in their hand and were about to toast to new friends. I assumed my post by the door.

After a round of toasts, the little man said something in Italian to his wife. She dug into the black handbag and pulled out a neat roll of twenty-dollar bills, tied with a piece of string. She nervously counted off six of the bills as we all watched. She then tied the tattered string around the remaining roll and placed them back in a compartment in the purse. She then counted them again and handed them over to her husband who leafed through them, counting once again. When they had finished, he handed the pile of bills to my dad. One hundred twenty dollars. I had counted the money each time they had, as had Dad and my mother. Dad handed the money to Mother who fingered through the stack again, one hundred twenty dollars. She then handed the pile to my father who leafed quickly through and passed it back.

"I believe, Mr. Castelli, that we have a problem. There seems to have been some sort of mistake. It seems to be an honest mistake, perhaps some sort of error in counting." Mr. Castelli's face was as red as the liquor in the wine bottle and Mother's was about the color of her white apron. She stopped short of putting the cash in her apron pocket and I knew what she was thinking. This was it, the trouble she had feared since we starting selling liquor from the back of the car. "Could you please count the money out on the table." He was looking directly at my mother who held the pile of twenties in an increasingly tight grip. My heart was pounding as I tried to plan my move. Did the Italian have a gun? It was doubtful since he wore no coat. What about the black purse? Mrs. Castelli clutched it so tightly. Was it large enough to carry a revolver? Would she know how to use it? I could sense trouble, although Dad's face was completely relaxed and his eyes seemed to have taken on a new glint. He drew a long breath and blew a cloud of cigar smoke into the room. The Italian woman nervously slipped a hand into the pocket from which she had retrieved the handkerchief. I watched the hand closely. Mother carefully laid the bills on the table, one by one, counting out loud as she went. "Twenty, forty, sixty, eighty, one hundred, one hundred twenty..." I felt my mouth gape as she laid six bills on the table, still holding a twenty-dollar bill in her hand. Mr. Castelli scowled at his wife who hung her head in embarrassment. Dad smiled a broad smile and winked at me. Mother leaned against the cupboard still holding the twenty-dollar bill and gave Dad a look that meant he would have to deal with her later. Dad picked up a twenty off the pile and handed it to the older man.

"I'm sure it was an honest mistake. I just didn't want any misunderstanding between us." Dad extended his large hand to the Italian who shook it rather sheepishly. Mr. Castelli issued a rather terse sounding statement in Italian to his wife as they turned to head out the door, throwing a 'thank you' over his shoulder.

Dad reached into the cupboard where he kept a genuine bottle of Irish malt whiskey and poured himself a glass and one for Mother. He waived the bottle my way but I politely declined, besides my hands were shaking so hard I think I'd have ended up wearing most of it. He raised the glass. "To the Italians." And downed the liquor. Mother set to finishing supper, scuttling about the kitchen and muttering to Dad while I slipped off to my room for a quick nap before tackling my homework.

Later that evening over a game of gin rummy, I asked Dad what had happened, where had the extra twenty come from.

"My hand," was his answer, I must have looked a little confused. "I palmed it. It's an old magician's trick. The most important thing with new business, especially this business is trust. They buy from Italians because they know that Italians aren't going to take advantage of them. I just showed that I'm not going to take him either. Sure, it cost me twenty bucks, but I'm sure I can more than make up for it. I hope you like spaghetti son, because we're eating with the Italians." With that he slapped his cards down on the table. "Gin."

SNOWBELL

By Denise M. Baran-Unland

The autumn rain splashed against the patio glass and trickled in silent streams to muddy pools near the sliding door. I stood unblinking and watched it, relieved for dry, cozy shelter, and yet wistful for the future my haughty recklessness had prematurely extinguished.

I closed my eyes and recalled another rainy day years ago when, sitting cross-legged in a circle on the cold tile floor of the kindergarten room, we answered our teacher's question, "What do you want to be when you grow up?"

Many of the replies included mommies, teachers, nurses, and stenographers, for this was nineteen fifty-eight and few girls in Grover's Park aspired to much more. I, however, had already visited Europe twice with my parents and was more intrigued with airline uniforms than with famous landmarks and old museums. I happily blurted, "Stewardess," but never in my most fanciful reveries did I imagine living out my days as a cat.

Looking back, the clues foreshadowing my destruction were everywhere, but how, then, was I to know they were harmful? All had logical explanations. The hypnotizing gray shadow flitting by an east, second floor mansion window was the result of a cloud passing near the sun. The leer from the short, faintly hunched businessman at Sue's Diner was merely the act of a dirty old man. The beckoning mist at the woods' edge around twilight was nothing more than cool water vapor, swirling as it met the day's humid air and condensed. To think I had once considered it provocative to hide behind the general store, necking and petting with the twenty-something lead singer from the centennial band!

At any point during my expedition into the woods I could have turned back, but there is something electrifying about roaming outdoors at night. Underneath the serenity of a starry sky, long after domesticated mortals have yawned and slunk to bed, another world of predatory creatures rises and begins their day. I'm not talking ghosts here, but ordinary beings: opossums, foxes, owls, and even bats. The alien sounds and shapes of the dark scared the other girls, but they enlivened me, and I ached to run free. Yet, even I wasn't foolish enough to enter a deteriorating building after midnight. I only planned to inhabit the grounds until dawn, the first person courageous enough in this hick little village to do it, and return with the triumphant report that the mansion's ghost legends were false.

It hadn't quite worked out that way.

I was blissfully tearing across the estate grounds, just past the ramshackle gazebo, when a shrill cry ripped into the night. Not a brief screech, such as one might hear from a barn owl, but a long, painful wail that escalated higher and higher until it ended in a bone-chilling shriek. I started, tripped,
and smacked face down into a half-buried cobble-stone. I lay, stunned, while the shock of the accident washed over me. My head throbbed, my skin smarted, and my limbs refused to move. I painfully sat up and gingerly shifted my arms and legs. Blood ran down my nose and trickled into my mouth. Great. My mother had been shopping my portfolio around, and three modeling agencies had already expressed interest. Worried, I sat on the damp ground for a long while and pressed my jacket sleeve across my face until the flow slowed. I briefly considered turning back but pride inter-vened, for I simply refused to become another victim of a small town myth. So I pressed my palms on the ground to steady myself, slowly stood, and gathered my bearings. The gazebo was behind me, on the left, which meant the mansion had to be straight ahead. I took a hesitant step. It didn't hurt as much as I expected, but running was obviously no longer possible. What did it matter? I had all night. As I hobbled toward the mansion, I kept a sharp lookout. What had caused that awful sound?

Just as I rounded the front of the old house, there was a crunching of tires and a bright beam of light. Had the girls called the police? As my eyes adjusted to the scene, I saw the vehicle was not a squad car. The door opened, and a man in a long, dark coat emerged. I recognized him immediately. He was the businessman scrutinizing me yesterday afternoon. I edged away, preparing to bolt, if necessary, confident that, even in my condition, I could outrun someone as old as he.

"Good Lord!" The man stepped closer and adjusted his horn-rimmed glasses. "It's the little girl from Sue's Diner."

The term "little girl" rankled me, and I momentarily lost my mistrust of him. Most people considered me older than seventeen, even when I wasn't wearing makeup, and the fact that he hadn't tried to sound condescending made it worse.

"Sir, you are trespassing on private property," I said in my most preemptory tone. I was, after all, an official guest and had the authority to make pronouncements. "I could have you arrested."

He threw back his head and laughed heartily. Apparently, he was too stupid to understand the trouble I could cause for him. "Arrest me! Little girl, you do realize I sit on the village board?"

Before I recovered from this shock, he peered closer and said, "You're bleeding."

Still? I dabbed my hand against my nose. His tone had been flat, unconcerned. He had made an observation, nothing more. Well, I wasn't worried, either. "It's nothing."

"Nonsense." He took a step forward, "and look how swollen that hand is. I noticed you limping, too. What happened? Did someone hurt you?"

"No, I fell." He was forcing me to answer questions, and I didn't like it. I was losing control of the situation. I had to regain it, quickly, but how?. The older people back home were easier to dismiss. "It's nothing," I repeated, but my objection sounded hollow and empty.

"Little girl, do you realize you might have a concussion, whiplash, or even a hairline fracture in your neck?"

I was tired of the phrase, "little girl," and I tossed my head defiantly to prove both my chagrin and the fact that nothing was broken. "I'm sure I'm fine," I said, all the while considering the merits of walking away from the building until he left. I had no intentions of returning to the servant's cottage until morning, but how would he know that?

"Nevertheless," he said. "I recommend you go inside and allow me to dress those wounds before I take you home."

Go inside the mansion? With *him*? I remembered the

smirking the way he had looked at Sue's Diner. Did he really think I was so naive? So what if he was a board member? Even if he could prove his mighty status, he certainly had no business on these grounds in the middle of the night. Technically, I didn't either, but I wasn't going to admit that. I shot a haughty, "I don't think so!" and started to limp away, but he stepped closer and laid a firm hand on my shoulder.

"I can't fix you up out here," he said with impatience.

I tried shaking him free, but he was obviously stronger than he looked. Instead, I looked at him with all the scorn I could muster. "I'm not going in there with you. Good night!"

"Look, you chit!"

He handed me a card, and I shuffled closer to the headlights to read it.

Dr. Abner Rothgard
Board certified in neurology, hematology, immunology,
cardiology, endocrinology, obstetrics, and veterinary and internal
medicine.

All right, so the man was no dummy, but I still felt cautious. What business would such a prestigious doctor have at the mansion and at this hour, too? I dropped the card and said, "If you're really doctor, why are you at the estate in the middle of the night?" Somehow, my words lacked the bite I hoped they'd have.

Dr. Rothgard shut off the ignition, grabbed his medical bag, and slammed the door. "Really, I should be asking you that question."

"I'm staying at the servant's cottage for the weekend." I put my hands on my hips, cocked my head, and said, "Your turn," hoping he'd act just a little intimidated.

"Heavens, what an impertinent child! Since you must know, I was securing the building for the night."

This time, I ignored his slam on my youth. "You couldn't do that during normal hours? The tours ended hours ago."

"A hospital emergency prevented it." Dr. Rothgard shook his head in what seemed to be a regretful manner. "I won't force you

84

to accept medical treatment, but as a doctor and village official, I do have to act. Therefore, I will simply contact the police and call for an ambulance. Good night." He turned toward his car.

"Wait!"

If he called the authorities, I would return as a laughingstock with my tail between my legs. I had never been humiliated, especially by an adult, and I had no intention of starting now. I thought fast. If I accepted his recommendation, I could afterwards pretend to go back, hide amongst the trees until he departed, and proceed with my scheme. Surely, he'd understand I couldn't accept a ride from a stranger, especially since I didn't have too far to walk. How likely was it that a man with his upstanding reputation in a tiny village should have evil intentions, especially a man wearing a black Pierre Cardin trench coat? I decided not too likely.

Dr. Rothgard slipped his hand into a deep coat pocket, brought forth a set of keys, and dangled them before my eyes. "It's the gold, old-fashioned one."

Really angry now at his arrogance, I snatch-ed the keys and gingerly stomped up the porch. The gold key fit perfectly; the ornate knob swung easily; and I pushed open the heavy door. The man was obviously trustworthy, but I still had to get rid of him, before he asked too many snoopy questions. Tomorrow, he'd probably have a moral fit and report me anyway, but why should I care? I'd be long gone.

Dr. Rothgard came up the stairs behind me. "Now then," he said. "Am I redeemed?"

"Maybe," I said, hoping levity would hasten the situation. "You haven't treated me yet."

"So, I haven't," Dr. Rothgard said, as he removed the keys from the lock and re-pocketed them, his eyes never leaving my face. Was he smiling or sneering? "But I soon shall."

I started to follow Dr. Rothgard into the mansion, but he raised a hand. "Wait here," he said. "No need for a second mishap. I will bring a light."

The darkness swallowed him in one gulp, and his footsteps faded into silence. The night was strangely still, and I wondered how late it now was since even the insects had ceased their chirping. The old gray stone building, with its hanging shutters and leaning porch, was the ideal setting for a horror movie, but only because of its remote location and poor condition, for I was still not afraid, only annoyed at this interruption in my plans. I knew ghosts did not exist and even the slim possibility of getting really hurt on the neglected estate had disappeared now that someone familiar with it was keeping me company, not that I'd share that piece of information when I returned to the other girls. A chill shuddered through me as the pre-dawn air cooled around me. I pulled my jacket collar over my neck and wished it was warmer. Perhaps, after the doctor had mended my wounds, I'd head for the broken-down gazebo. It might be less drafty than spending the rest of the night in the open. A white cat slipped around the mansion's corner. I blinked, but the creature was gone. Had I imagined it? Then I heard a meow, but it was only the creaking of the old floor. A wafting light sliced through the blackness. Dr. Rothgard had returned, carrying a long, taper candle in one hand and a cloth bag in the other.

"Follow me," he said, handing me the bag, "and keep this on your nose."

Dr. Rothgard turned left and led me into a room at the front of the house. I meekly placed the ice pack on my nose and shuffled after him. I wondered for a quick moment where he had gotten ice in this broken-down, forsaken place, then foolishly decided good doctors simply came prepared to do their jobs in all circumstances. I sneezed twice under my ice pack as I entered the room, then saw why. Thick dust smothered the parlor carpet, heavy curtains, upholstery, and the curved, wooden legs of the many chairs and tables. Lacy cobwebs swathed the silver picture frames, the blue vases on the mantle, and the pink bric-a-brac. Dust webs hung in long strands from the oil lamps, like tinsel on a Christmas tree. Dr. Rothgard gestured to a two-seater couch near the fireplace.

"Sit down," he said.

"On that dirty thing?" I began, until I remembered my ruined clothes. Two hundred dollars at Miss Emmaline's Boutique, gone. My zeal for spending the night at a reputedly haunted mansion had faded. I was bone tired and eager to get the examination finished as quickly as possible. Wearily, I dropped onto the couch. I couldn't wait to curl up somewhere, anywhere, and go to sleep.

Dr. Rothgard squatted in front of me. "Slip off your shoes."

My shoes? Why my shoes? It was my nose that was bleeding. For the first time since I had run off, I hesitated. My confidence at outwitting Dr. Rothgard was ebbing. Somehow, I had lost my advantage over him. Perhaps, I never really had it? I clenched my toes, for he must not see my shaking and think he intimidated me. Then, I caught a lingering scent of fine pipe tobacco, and I relaxed. He didn't stink of cigarettes like my parents did. Inwardly, I scolded myself. I had allowed the combination of fatigue, the room's eeriness, and local legend to overwhelm sound judgment. Dr. Rothgard had seen it hurt to walk. He was just being a doctor; that was all. I pried away first one shoe, and then the other. He picked up my left foot. I winced, but did not pull away. Beginning with the toes, Dr. Rothgard pressed gently all over my foot, ending at my swollen ankle.

"Nothing's broken," he said, "only sprained."

He repeated the process with my right foot, and I relaxed. He was simply a harmless country doctor. I should be thankful for his help. Why spend the rest of the night unnecessarily hurting? How victorious would I look in the morning, bruised and banged up? Dr. Rothgard moved the ice pack to my swollen hand.

"Hold it here," he said.

With easy, practiced fingers, Dr. Rothgard felt along the bridge of my nose and down both sides.

"Nothing's broken," he said, "and the bleeding has finally stopped. You don't want to do that here, you know. It's very dangerous."

I nearly laughed aloud. Who really was the gullible one? "It's dangerous to bleed? In this mansion? Don't tell me you believe the ghost legend, too!"

Dr. Rothgard stopped, fingers resting lightly on my cheeks, and looked sharply at me. "Do you take me for a fool? Haven't you realized you're miles away from the nearest hospital!"

Before I could retort, he placed his hands firmly on each side of my neck. "Does this hurt?"

An odd twist, a paroxysm of pain, a loud snap, and the wildly spinning room sucked me into a swirling tunnel of darkness. Giant falcons ripped through curtains of black and encircled me.; razors pecked at me; jaws clamped my leg, but as I kicked the large, black beetle, a snake wrapped around me and stared up with glowing, yellow eyes. Another doleful wail and an emaciated form floated past, swiping the air with clawed, skeletal fingers. A platform raised, and thousands of white cats in black choir robes stood and screamed. Moaning wisps melted in hoary, dripping streams. Miles ahead, a bright light blinked, then vanished. I tumbled down, down, down and landed with a hard thump. Four hands lifted me up and moved me through dripping water and moldy dampness. The light grew closer. Identical angels froze in various postures. Hundreds of candles winked their greetings. Was this heaven?

"She's waking," Dr. Rothgard said behind me.

A siren rang. Red lights flashed. The medic on my right was tall with long, blond hair and looked as if he hated the world. The second attendant had dark hair and a slight build.

"What happened?" asked the first.

"She fell," his companion replied.

The door shut, and the ambulance squealed into the night. An intravenous needle poured bloody fluid into my neck. I squirmed against the pain; two hands pushed me back and held me in place.

"My neck," I moaned. "It hurts."

"You mustn't speak," the dark-haired para-medic said, with a warning glance at his co-worker.

I closed my eyes and settled into their care. For once in my life, I felt genuinely thankful for help, for loving friends, and for hospitals. The local idiots would blame my misfortune on the ghost. Well, I would worry about that later. Maybe, I could concoct a story about a band of vicious....

A hard jerk. My eyes flew open. A thermometer slid into my mouth. A cuff wrapped around my arm. A tube slipped past my nose and into my throat. I raised my eyes to the mirror above and saw my battered and swollen face. My worried parents hovered over me.

"You had us so scared," my mother quavered, rubbing my arm and trying to smile through her tear-streaked face. Her pancake makeup had cracked in several places; a false eyelash was halfway peeled off. Despite her tangerine Pucci pantsuit and platinum bleached hair, my mother looked old.

My father, his own Pierre Cardin trench coat, beige, unbuttoned and crumpled, patted my head as if he would never stop. His toupee had slid over one ear and his gray mustache quivered. "Thank God, you're all right!"

Well, God had nothing to do with it, and I tried to tell them so, but my voice wouldn't utter a single syllable. I glanced at the machine on my left. A single line moved across it. I opened my mouth to scream. That's when I realized I wasn't breathing, not one single breath. I bore down hard, but my chest muscles didn't budge. Yet, my parents still smiled benignly at me.

"What would we have done without Dr. Rothgard?" my mother said.

"Yes, what could we have done?" my father echoed.

Dr. Rothgard?

The doors flew open, and Dr. Rothgard, clad in green scrubs, strode into the room. He was real?

"No!" I shouted, but no sound passed my lips. I tried grabbing my mother's sleeve, but my arm wouldn't work. Please, I silently begged her. Please, don't let him do anything to me. Please, make him go away.

She must have noticed my distress, for she smiled encouragingly at me. "It's all right," my mother said. "You just need a little transfusion."

A transfusion? So, I wasn't dead, after all? Would a transfusion restore my heartbeat? Could it make me breathe? Was this normal hospital procedure? A musky-scented mask slipped over my nose, and a white cat scampered out of the room.

"One got away," my father said, smiling.

"That's all right," Dr. Rothgard said. "There's more."

Beyond me were hundreds of beds. On each bed lay a white cat. Tubes poured red fluid from them into me. Was that cat blood? I looked up at the mirror. My nose had shrank and turned pink. White fur sprouted on my cheeks. Laughter rang in my ears, and I spun around. One of the pirates pointed and said, "Aw, I told you it was her."

The gorilla nodded and shoved another handful of potato chips between his rubber lips.

I ran the back of my furry hand across my dripping forehead and seriously considered changing out of my costume. The bright yellow and orange walls reminded me of summer campfires, except the colors hurt my eyes and made them water. I pushed through the apple bobbing line toward the snack table. No one else seemed to mind the heat, but then, no one else wore a fur-lined cat costume. God, it was hot! I hoped the ice chest was full.

Sitting at the round game table at the far end of the room, just past the food and beverage area, was my friend Melissa. She was wearing a faded Victorian gown and playing cards with a caped figure opposite her. I grabbed two handfuls of ice and rubbed them across my face and along my neck. The ice instantly melted under my scorching skin, but I felt slightly cooler. If only my neck didn't throb so much.

I wandered to the card table and peered over the caped form's shoulder at the cards, and the figure turned. There was no one inside that cape, no one at all. I gasped and woke up.

Dr. Rothgard had pulled up a chair beside the couch and was sitting, watching me and contentedly puffing on his pipe. The fireplace crackled high. I pushed away a blanket and started to sit, but my head pounded and whirled. Queasy, I settled back into the seat cushions and heard the chiming tinkle of a piano. Some else was here, too? I looked at Dr. Rothgard. "Who's playing the piano?"

He lowered his pipe and listened for a long minute. "I don't hear anything."

Dr. Rothgard lowered a green sprig with fuzzy gray-green, heart-shaped leaves over my face. It had the same heady, musky smell as the hospital mask. As I blissfully inhaled it, my lungs expanded and contracted. *I was breathing!* I panted with delight.

"How do you feel?" Dr. Rothgard asked.

"Very strange," I said, still happily huffing and puffing. "Weak, and yet...."

"And yet...what?" He moved the greenery closer, and I

90

swiped it. Quickly, Dr. Rothgard moved it out of reach. The piano notes scurried up then crept back, like tiptoeing mice.

"I feel strangely invigorated."

"Hmmm." Dr. Rothgard dropped the plant back into his bag and reached for the ice pack on the floor. "I'll return shortly."

The lovely notes were softer now, yet definitely unmistakable.

Dr. Rothgard was obviously covering for someone. I dug my elbows into the cushion and swung my legs off the couch; my head whirled with the effort. The piano played slowed, halting, wistful. I stood still, teetering, wondering if I could remain upright. Dr. Rothgard would return any second. I had to hurry. Gripping the furniture for balance, I tottered into the hall. The music stopped, and I heard footsteps. Sweat rolled down my face. I wasn't ready for him yet. Which way? I waddled to the grand staircase, dropped to my hands and knees, and crept up the hard wood stairs. At the second floor, I scampered around the corner and crouched
there, panting for wonderful breath and
congratulating myself at outsmarting Dr. Rothgard.

The door to an east-end rooms was ajar. Moonlight filtered through a cracked window and cast pale bands across the carpet. I heard mur-muring voices and again saw Melissa, dressed in that shabby Victorian gown and walking, trance-like, across the room. I softly called her name, but she did not answer. So, I rose to follow her.

I entered the parlor just as she settled on the couch. A tea tray materialized on the sidebar next to me. I poured a glass of water for me and a cup of tea for my friend. A skeleton sprang up, snatched away the items, and gave the tea to Melissa. She raised the cup to her lips. It was filled with blood.

I leaped onto the couch just as the skeleton, teeth bared, was leaning forward to bite her. Melissa choked and blood splattered onto her dress and across the skeleton's face. A bony arm slammed me to the floor; my head banged against a kitchen cabinet; and my fangs sank into a huge rat.

The free-floating parlor dust swirled in the early morning light like a gentle snowfall. I shivered and pulled up the afghan. The fire was out. Dr. Rothgard's head flopped over the back of his chair. I cautiously stretched each limb, but nothing hurt anymore, except my neck, and that only felt stiff, not sore.

Dr. Rothgard grunted and snorted. His eyes fluttered open and immediately rested on me. He leaned forward and motioned for me to come closer. "Let's take a listen to you."

I obediently slid to the edge of the couch and sat quite still as Dr. Rothgard listened to my heart and lungs. When he had finished, Dr. Roth-gard looked at me long and hard.

"Well," he said. "You look better. How do you feel?"

"Rested," I said, but I immediately knew that was the wrong word. "Rejuvenated."

Dr. Rothgard smiled, but it was a sardonic half-smile. I couldn't tell if my answer pleased him or not. He replaced the stethoscope, snapped the medical bag shut, and rose. "You're positive you don't want a ride?"

"No," I said, still feeling wary. Last night's dream hung heavy around me.

"Please yourself," he said. "I don't suppose there's any danger, now that it's day."

"Then I'm free to go? You won't try to stop me?"

"Of course you're free to go," Dr. Rothgard said scornfully. "You always have been."

I backed away, toward the door, expecting him to hamper my escape, but Dr. Rothgard was poking around the fireplace, making sure no embers remained. I fled to the front door, flung it open, and bolted down the steps. Without a single look back, I flew across the estate into the thicker part of the woods. It would take me longer to return this way, but it would be impossible for Dr. Rothgard to track me. Yet, he didn't seem to care I had left. Why should he? Obviously, the horror of the previous night was the result of my overactive imagination. I laughed aloud, triumphantly. I had survived the night. I couldn't wait to gloat and receive the lauds due me. I had one over the villagers. Cowards!

The early morning chatter contrasted with last night's stark silence. I never knew woods could be so noisy, low groaning mixed with the clacking of jaws, along with cawing, chirping, and cooing.

92

Even the tweeting of the birds that had not flown south for the winter was deafening. Lake Munson hungrily lapped the shore. Men murmured quite close to my ears, yet I saw no one. A giant rabbit roared past me, and I stood motionless until my racing, thumping heart calmed down. I was more overtired than I thought, but that was easily fixed by napping later this morning, on the drive back to Grover's Park. Trees towered overhead, much higher than when I had first ventured into the woods. Dried foliage swished against my waist and tangled around my burning ankles and knees. I smelled strong coffee and the warm, buttery scent of Brian's toast, comforting reminders of imminent safety. I swayed and dug my heels into the ground, but they would no longer support my weight. The clearing was ahead. The servant's cottage was in full view. I had made it back, just as I had hoped, but it was too late. With a little cry, I dropped to the ground and ran the rest of the way on all four white paws.

SOMA

By Lindsay Lake

Tiny dirt tornados spun on top of hard packed sand.

A crack appeared, and then another, and another, until the mound moved and erupted under a great force from beneath.

The crackling savanna sun touched the flesh of the man.

His body spasmed. He gulped in the air. Sand flew from his nostrils and mouth. His arms and legs flailed uncontrollably, like a seizure overtook his body. His lungs expanded and he lived.

He yelled out with each breath as if in pain.

Bugs crawled over the dirt on his skin and stuck to the hair on his body. He panicked and brushed at them with wild fury. His hands flew to his face and he brushed the bugs from his eyes, his nose, and his mouth. He opened his eyes. He held his hand in front of his face. He touched his arms and his legs, his chest, thighs and groin. He ran his hands through the hair on his head and bugs flew every which way.

He did not know where he was, who he was, what he was, or where he came from.

He trembled.

He dropped to his knees, brushing the sand and bugs from between his legs. He wrapped his arms around himself as if to keep warm or to stop shaking. He touched the ground in front of him. He held his abdomen and coughed many times, spitting and brushing the dirt from his face with his saliva.

His body stuck to the ground in some way. He lay a hand on the ground, and his hand stuck there. He picked his hand up and looked at it. He placed it on the ground again. He picked up balls of dirt and held them at eye level. He turned his hand over and the dirt balls fell to the ground. He repeated this action many times, always with the same results. He adjusted to gravity.

He watched the wind blow the dust and dirt from his shins. He felt the hair on his legs move like the sand in the wind. As he batted the bugs, he hit at the wind. But the wind blew in multiple

94

directions. He felt the wind on his face, and shoulders, and blow through his hair. He turned and turned again, only to find nothing there. No assailant. He stared into the wind and shut his eyes. He filled his lungs with the wind; a pleasant feeling; a pleasant smell. He assisted the wind with his hands brushing the dirt from his face. He shook and scratched his head and still bugs flew in each direction but the friendly wind carried them off somewhere.

Bugs crawling over him could drive him mad. Could drive him back underground. He brushed and brushed his head, chest, and legs. With the help of the wind he felt debugged and his apprehension lessened.

He fought with gravity and stood on his own two feet. North, south, east, and west, all looked the same; a dry, flat savanna with an occasional sprig of foliage. As far as he could see, and he could see an eternity in each direction.

He stood alone.

Alone in a vast wasteland.

A sound came from his mouth.

He screamed.

He screamed again.

Afraid of his own voice; he stuffed his fingers into his mouth, silencing himself. Distracted, he felt his teeth and his tongue and the moisture there.

He found the source of the pleasant warmth on his skin. He turned toward the sun. He walked into the wind and toward the light. With each exhale he squeaked out a little moan.

His arms and legs grew stronger with each step. He walked a long way in some direction.

His long hair made a shade over his eyes from the relentless sun. A consistent breeze lifted his thick hair, evaporating the perspiration there.

He walked the deserted sand trails heavy with bugs; always bugs. He caught them. He ate them.

He followed the sun until it grew so dark he could not see. He thought he died.

He covered himself with sand and dirt and slept.

He woke not remembering the day before.

He marveled at how strong and muscular his body grew.

He ran fast.

He had the ability to walk an indefinite distance at a steady pace.

Something walked the sandy soil with him - slithered beside him. He grabbed the snake like he did the bugs, to eat it, and it bit him. The snake bit him many times before he killed it. He sickened but he ate the snake anyway.

His legs swelled twice their size, cracked open and yellow liquid ran on to the sand. His whole body swelled and he lay down to die.

Flies attacked him, as they always did when not in motion. They did not attack him to bite him, they attacked him to eat the dead flesh from his body. They ate the puss and infection from the snake bites. He watched them. He felt no pain and had no will to stop them. He panicked when the flys entered his nose and ears to clean up there. His legs operated again and he walked toward the sun and the wind.

Birds attacked him. He killed one and ate it but he did not like that.

His body felt strange. His body held a mystery.

He walked to a tropical forest. Intense smells and soothing sounds of the moist leaves rubbing together attracted him. There were many bugs and plants to eat and water to drink but the creatures there were more vicious than he. He was attacked. He was bitten. He was scratched. He was tracked and hunted.

He, and other animals, were kept prisoner for food by a wolf pack. The other animals had large sharp teeth and powerful extremities with long claws but they were hysterical. They shrieked into the night as one by one, they were picked off by the wolf pack and eaten. The man sat with large eyes watching. He was silent. He watched for the moment the wolves were distracted and he got away.

The tropical jungle held much moisture. Fungus grew on him. His flesh rotted from sores on his body. Everywhere he walked he received little scratches into his skin that festered. He could not trust the trees, or the grass to even sit and rest upon, for they held the ability to slice his skin, pierce his skin, and suck his blood. He

96

could not stop it. In the thick jungle he could not find the sun. He whimpered and cried when the sun faded, mourning the loss. Liquid fell from his eyes and down his cheeks. He picked up the liquid with his tongue. It tasted good. He fell into an untenable situation. He beat his way through the jungle going he knew not where.

He had a thought. He remembered the dry savanna. He could find a better place. Maybe, if he could get somewhere he could win, or be safe, or something. He climbed the tallest hill.

One moment, and one moment only, OBJ he lay on the hill top. Lush, new growth, long green grass laid over the expanse of the hill. He relaxed his body. The sun hit his flesh in delightful places. He turned in on himself. He wrapped himself up in himself. The rays of the sun pierced his eyes forcing him to shut them. He saw colors through his eyelids and he let the phosphines dance. A gentle wind blew his hair across his face in a pleasant way. He warmed up. Nothing crawled on him. Nothing besieged him. Nothing pressed him into action. Neither too hot nor too cold. He experienced comfort. His jaw relaxed and his mouth opened and he took in copious amounts of the sweet warm air. His hair danced on his lips like a playmate tickling him. He made a noise as close to a laugh as he ever would. His muscular shoulders relaxed and he let loose of himself and his arms fell onto the grass and he felt the moisture of the healthy blades. His hands reached for pleasure. He ripped the grass from its roots and smeared the grass over his face and mouth, down his chest and abdomen. The tube between his legs grew three times its size and he put the cool grass on himself to calm himself. He felt a warm tingle and rubbed more grass. The tube grew not larger in size but larger in intensity. A wave controlled his body and his mind. He took in great gulps of air. His body shook with an ancient rhythm that erupted in a thoughtless, mindless, timeless explosion. He yelled out into the void. Bird calls answered back as they rushed to identify the song they heard. He listened to his heart beating in his ears. He ran his hand over his body and tickled his chest and abdomen. He felt his neck and face, his mouth, his tongue. The grass on his hands was moist with a glistening substance and he stuffed the grass into his mouth. If something felt that good, the substance must be good to eat. His body writhed and rocked in

97

residual pleasure. He rolled onto his side, into the fetal position, with one hand between his legs holding himself and his other hand in his mouth. He licked and sucked the fat pad on his thumb.

He breathed in the scent of the sweet grass.

His feet danced against each other, petting and soothing each other. His toes played together like children. He could only think back a few minutes. He thought of how the birds reacted to his loud roar of pleasure. The corners of his mouth may have turned up somewhat. He rubbed his fingers over his lips and gazed out over the waves of grass, the occasional jump of a grasshopper, or the movement of a bird or rabbit.

There comes a time in every day when the sun is bright but fails to warm the skin; when this happened he thought he lay too long. A large ant bit him. He slapped his shin and put the ant in his mouth. It was big. It was red. It was juicy. It was good to eat. But the ant had broken his skin and there was another ant, and another, and another. He ate, and ate, and ate, but soon they came so fast they covered his body. He ran from the hill. The ants stuck to his body not wanting to give up a good meal. They stung him.

He came upon a pool of water and threw himself in. The water's cool temperature felt good on his bites. His blood ran into the water. He felt a little fish nibbling at his toes and legs. They tickled him. But the fish were not happy with just his blood; they wanted his flesh too and they bit him. He threw himself onto the muddy bank. He forgot his one precious moment of comfort ever existed. The mud felt good on his bites and he rubbed the mud onto the skin on his legs, arms, face and neck.

The pool of water churned with activity waiting for his return. Their splashing sounded like little voices calling to him.

The sun dropped low in the sky. He tried to follow along the banks of the muddy pool until the last bit of sunlight. 'Come back, come back.' They seemed to say.

He came to a clear lake. He could see the full horizon. His anxieties dissipated. He sat on the bank. The mud dried and cracked on his skin. He picked at it. He looked into the still clear waters and saw his reflection. What a flimsy weak creature he was. No claws, no fangs, no fur, nothing to defend or protect himself with, but his eyes shined as clear blue as the sky, and his skin glowed the color of the sand, so he knew he belonged to the earth.

His eyes held a hint of intelligence; if he could build a fortress around himself . . . .

He stacked some branches and large leaves and crawled inside to die again, as the sun faded and the day was done. He watched the last light leave the sky through the cracks of his barricade.

The next day he walked until his feet swelled, turned red, burst open and liquid ran out. At times the tube between his legs hurt a bit. Another fluid came out of his tube that was yellow; that felt good too, but not as good as the white. Every day foul material fell out of him. He thought he was poisoned. He thought he was rotting from within. He had an opinion of himself as a diseased, dirty, organism of the lowest order.

He traveled to a huge body of water with waves splashing. He ran right in. He floated. He swam. This was the place he dreamed of. Birds followed him in a friendly way. He smiled and laughed and sang back to them. The birds didn't attack him. Looked like these creatures had enough to eat for they left him alone for a long, long time. His body swelled from the salt water. He stayed so long in the water he could hardly walk on land. He crawled and moved anyway he could. He tried to put braces on his legs with branches and vines. He took a stick to help him walk. He grew so sick he threw up. Brown liquid rushed out of him from other holes in him. Even the tube.

He came upon a mountain. He crawled up the mountain. Days turned into weeks, to months, to years, he traveled. He felt if he could get to the top, he would be where he should be. Just one more inch. Just one more day. He pushed himself. He got to the top by extraordinary measures; destroying his body to get there. The higher he climbed the less birds, less insects, less pestilence he encountered.

Things dried out.

His body grew smaller, weaker, and much more painful. He had a vague memory of his body being young and strong.

He had a big thought; if he could rest a moment he may heal and be something again.

At the top of the mountain the air smelled sweet, clean and fresh. He could see the sun from the moment it rose until the moment it set. A calmness washed over him. Nothing lived on the mountain but some bird nests above him, and a stream of water that trickled down the mountain side. One large bird floated lazily in the sky.

He made a nest for himself, like the birds, and lay to rest. He did not move for so long he could not move. He drank from the stream and ate an occasional bird egg that fell from the nests above him. He did not move through intense heat and frigid cold. His legs were still for so long; he watched them disintegrate in front of his eyes. He sank into the dirt. His body rotted. He watched his toes eaten by birds and maggots. At last, he knew the feeling of being wanted.

His limbs useless. He existed by a shallow inspiration and expiration of breath and a faint beat of his heart, but always, his clear blue eyes searching the sky for the sun to come up and be his friend. What was left of him turned to dust. Nothing remained but dirt on the mountain side.

The sun passed over the horizon uncountable times. Many big birds flew over the mountain.

One day, under the nest of many birds, by the trickle of a mountain stream, the earth cracked open and the flesh of a man could be seen as he struggled to gasp his first breath.

THE SWING

By Sharon Houk

"Because he knew what it was like to suffer." This is what she said aloud when looking at Fragonard's painting The Swing at the National Gallery of Art. No one in the gallery paused or turned to look. Everyone had heard her. She had said it quite loudly.

In the same gallery, an old lady with an umbrella was worrying about her dog and thought that the forest in the painting looked so big and unknowable – like a galaxy that could swallow you up. The swing, a pendulum, would swoop you backwards into the darkness and then bring you forward again into the light. Just that morning, her little dog had eaten something, that very morning he had eaten something – that had made him cough. It was in the cough that she came to understand that he was mortal. Cough. Cough. Before that, he had just been her dog. But now he was her dog that would someday die. And when that someday arrives, she will feel herself swinging into the great clouded unknown of all the darkness of her childhood and all the loneliness of her now.

In the same gallery, a man wanted to get his hands into the underpants of the woman he was with. He didn't care about the paintings or the museum or her. He pretended to look at The Swing. He wondered how he could manage to get her to pay for lunch. He wondered how long he would have to walk around pretending to be interested in any of this old tat. It was crowded and hot. That morning, he'd pretended to lose his car key so that she had to drive them to the museum and pay for parking. Bitch. How stupid can you get? He could put her on a swing. And choke her. She looked at him as if he were actually hearing her. Her lips were moving.

In the same gallery, a child thought The Swing was the most beautiful picture they had ever seen. Such a big swing. The child could smell the day, the grass, the breeze, the dirt when you drag

101

your feet, the sunshine in the moment when you are weightless, the moment at the top, the moment between going higher and coming back down. That's when the sunshine tastes the best: at the top. The child's legs knew how to push hard to swing higher, lean forward and pitch back and point your toes up up, and the child ran around the room ebullient with the knowledge of a perfect swinging technique, squealing and dashing around its mother and siblings and screaming in delight. Someone from a nearby room turned to look.

THE BEL AIR

By Steven James Cordin

Gary Perch managed to get out of working crowd control at the plaza but decided to go over there anyway to watch the big man. Then he saw the black Bel Air.

Lieutenant Baxter wanted him to stay for a second morning shift to work the crowd, but Perch begged off. The lieutenant already scheduled him working Thanksgiving night the following week, and his wife would be upset if he missed spending the day with her and the kids. He got home that morning only to find Peggy packing Johnnie and May into the Packard.

"We are going to Plano." Peggy told him. "It's my sister's birthday. Are you coming?"

Perch shook his head. "I need to get some sleep. I have the night shift this week."

Peggy frowned at her husband, disappointed that his schedule didn't get any better since making detective a year ago. She sighed and pecked him on the cheek. Perch went to bed as the Packard roared off.

He lay in bed for an hour before realizing he wouldn't get any sleep. He got up, made some eggs, and dressed in a grey shirt with khaki trousers. Around nine, he jumped in his Ford and drove downtown. Silly man, Peggy's voice echoed in his head, you should have just gone to Plano.

He parked a few blocks from the plaza and walked over to Carl's Diner. Friday traffic appeared heavier than usual and the traffic cop at the corner appeared worn and tired. Perch smiled to himself, glad he left that part of the job with his promotion to detective. Carl's sat on a street just behind the plaza. He strolled in as the jukebox played the last chords of a song Peggy loved, Needles and Pins. A new tune, He's so Fine, rolled on after it.

Perch grabbed a booth next to the plate glass window that ran next to the street. He ordered coffee and home fries. Only two other customers from the breakfast crowd remained. Perch enjoyed sitting here between the breakfast and lunch rush. He could relax and watch the world go by behind the window.

He planned to hang out at the diner for an hour and then head across to the plaza to watch the festivities. He gazed out the window and watched people pass by, going about their daily routine. The day turned out to be nice, the sky clear and warm.

His third cup of coffee sat on the table when he noticed the Bel Air. He began to doze off as he sat there staring out into the street. He would have missed it except the driver opened the trunk, causing a reflection of light that attracted Perch's gaze and woke him.

A '57 Black Bel Air with a white hardtop parked across the street. Perch recognized the car since he pulled it over twice in his police career. More importantly, he recognized the tall thin figure that opened the car's trunk.

Al Ricci.

Perch frowned and glared through the window at the man he arrested twice. What was he doing here? Perch questioned Ricci four months ago about shaking down a local bar, but the owner refused to identify him. Prior to that, he picked Ricci up regarding a shooting on the east side, but the charges didn't stick. Perch knew Ricci, a minor hood in the local rackets trying to make a name for himself. Perch watched as Ricci rummaged around in the trunk of his car until he finally pulled out a black guitar case. Perch's eyes narrowed into hard slits and his hands balled into fists.
Ricci is no musician, and I bet that isn't a guitar.

He threw three dollars on the table and turned from the window. He grimaced at the out of order sign hanging from the pay phone. No time anyway. He waved at Carl the owner, an overweight old man by the register.

"Carl, call the local station house. Tell them a detective needs assistance at that office building that Black Bel Air is parked in front of." He pointed towards the window and waited till Carl nodded he understood. "Give them my name and badge number. Two-four-six-nine."

Outside, Perch caught a glimpse of the door to the office building closing behind someone. He jogged across the street,

104

ignoring the blaring horns that filled the air. He looked up the street for the traffic cop, only to find him gone. At the entrance, he paused to rest his hand on the handle of his service pistol that hugged his hip. He slipped into the entrance, sure there was no time to wait for back up.

Perch blinked a few times as his eyes adjusted to the harsh light of the lobby's fluorescents overhead. He saw an elevator door slide close on the far wall. He hurried over and watched the needle above the doors slowly work its way up to the sixth floor. He glanced around for another elevator and saw none. He ran over to the stairs and began to climb.

He raced up the stairs, glad he ran four miles a day. Still, at the top of the sixth floor, he dripped with sweat and staggered to a stop. His heart raced as he gulped in deep gasps of air for a minute.

He stared down the dark hallway. Dead silence, the floor seemed deserted. Perch could only see three doors in the hall, but which did Ricci go in? Perch walked slowly through, the hall, blood roaring through his ears. He unholstered his pistol, the grip felt slick in his fingers.

Perch stopped at the third door, Meretti Exports stenciled on the frosted glass pane. Meretti, a businessman connected to organized crime, employed Ricci as a driver. The doorknob turned quietly, and Perch slipped in.

Silly man, Peggy's voice boomed in his head, you should wait for back up. He wanted Ricci though. This could jump start his career if Ricci was into something heavy.

Perch stopped in the foyer, letting his eyes take in the gloomy interior. Pale sunlight streamed in through dirty windows along the main room's opposite walls. A huge space that stretched across half the floor, appeared as deserted as the hallway. Several desks lay cast about the space haphazardly.

Meretti must have closed the office down some time ago. Need to be quiet so Ricci doesn't spot me.

Perch's eyes became drawn to a brighter patch of light among the windows. An open window. Beneath it, Ricci sat on the floor putting together a rifle and scope.

Jesus Christ.

The parade in the plaza. The motorcade.

That is crazy!

Perch slowly inched his way closer to Ricci, trying to make as little noise as possible. Until the metallic clatter of a waste can he tipped over echoed across the room. Ricci's chin rose from his rifle. Their eyes met and both men froze. Ricci moved first, rolling behind a nearby desk.

Perch dropped behind another desk. The desk shuddered against his back as a bullet buried itself into the front oak panel. A twenty-two or a thirty-eight. The top of the desk exploded and rained splinters on Perch as two more shots skimmed the top of it.

Silence for a few seconds. "Perch? Is that you?"

The horrid stench of cordite burned Perch's nose. "Yep."

"What the hell you doing here?"

"I was at Carl's having some coffee and I saw your Bel Air. I thought I would come over and see if you wanted to join me?"

Ricci's laugh sounded more like a donkey's bray to Perch. "Tell you what. Why don't you go back across the street and wait for me? I won't be but a few minutes here."

"I can't do that Ricci."

"Sure, you can." Ricci's smooth voice sounded like the used car salesman Peg bought the Packard from. "Look. I got something real important to do here. And I am making a lot of money. We can make a deal."

Perch wiped the sweat off his brow. "Got a better deal. Why don't you put the gun down and we go down to the precinct to talk about it?"

Now there was no emotion in Ricci's voice. "I can't do that Perch."

"Then we sit here till back up arrives. You can't win."

"Hey Perch? Have you ever seen the kind of damage a rifle can do at short range?"

Oh shit.

Perch flattened himself to the ground right before the left side of the desk exploded. He screamed as splinters of wood peppered his legs. Perch couldn't hear the second shot which disintegrated the legs on the left side of the desk, but his hip burned where a huge chunk of wood ripped into him. The desk tottered to the left but remained upright.

Perch could only hear the ringing in his ears. Cordite stung his eyes. He saw to his right the garbage can he kicked over earlier. He picked it up awkwardly and tossed it in the air. Then he rolled to his left clear of the desk. Ricci stood up behind his desk. trying to take a bead on the can with his rifle.

Perch sat up and squeezed off two shots. Ricci spun around and dropped behind the desk.

Perch fell back. He lay there for a while, choking on cordite.

Perch laid on the floor for a long time. Backup will be here any minute. After a while, Perch decided back up wasn't coming, so he needed to move.

The desk wobbled as he used it to pull himself up. He climbed to his feet, wincing at the sting in his legs and hip. He slowly limped to the open window, gun extended in both hands. Peg was laughing at him from the back of his mind. Silly man. If Ricci could, he would have blown your head off already.

Ricci wasn't in any shape to blow anyone's head off. He lay prone on the floor between the desk he used as cover and the wall. Blood seeped from his chest and made the floor sticky. He looked up at Perch with alert eyes though. The pistol and the rifle out of reach.

Perch leaned against the windowsill. "Hey."

"Hey."

"What the hell was this all about?"

Blood flecked Ricci's lips. Perch barely heard him over the ringing in his ears. "The guy...building across...street..."

Perch gazed out the window at the building across the street. Nothing. "What guy?"

Ricci stared up with vacant eyes. Gone.

Perch slumped against the desk. The ringing in his ears slowly changed to the murmur of the growing crowds outside. Perch went to the window and studied the plaza as the motorcade came into view.

It doesn't make any sense. There is no way to get a clear shot at the motorcade from this window, if that is what he wanted.

You could get a better shot from across the street at the book depository.

THE FIRST TIME...

By Tom Hernandez

"Oh my god," Louie Jackson said. "I am so embarrassed, and so sorry, Mrs. Anderson!"

Jackson's head dropped, his chin nearly touching his neck which now blossomed in fiery, red-hot shame. He seemed to fold into himself as his chest and abdomen deflated like a popped balloon.

"It's Ms. Anderson. I am divorced. And no need to apologize, Mr. Jackson. It happens all the time."

Louie lifted his eyes only high enough to see the look on the nurse's face. Attractive in the mature, slightly wrinkled way of experienced, middle-aged women confident in their authority and knowledge, she smiled a toothy grin of reassurance.

"Ok, but...I mean..." Louie couldn't control his stammer. "At his age? I mean...Jesus...he's ninety-seven years old. I didn't think those parts even work anymore." He shifted in his chair, trying to relieve some of the ache now creeping up his lower back. "And with the dementia and all?"

Again, she smiled. Louie caught himself staring at her eyes which seemed to sparkle. They were violet, like...like Elizabeth Taylor's eyes! Wow, he thought, if she weren't taking care of my grandfather, I might just...Her honeyed voice, practiced in soothing confused patients and their anxious family members, snapped him out of his temporary fugue.

"Absolutely! Sexual urges and thoughts are usually one of the last things to go. But let's be clear. Your grandpa didn't actually try to have sex with anyone – although that has happened, too. " She lowered her eyes and grinned, almost coy, and tittered. "Usually though, it's the women who try to initiate sex. I know you wouldn't think so, but it's true. One time, I walked into a patient's room only to find her on her knees between a male patient's legs doing...well, let's just say he may not have understood what was happening at that moment, but that's a memory he won't forget!"

Louie guffawed like a mule that'd been kicked in the hind quarters. "Really?"

One hundred percent true," she insisted. "But anyway, back to your grandfather. He wasn't doing anything. Rather, he is telling stories about his sexual exploits to anyone who will listen. The nurses don't mind so much. Like I said, we've all heard and seen it all before. But he's upset some of the other staff – especially the dining room attendants who are mostly young girls," Nurse Anderson said. "Funny thing is, these girls today, they think they know everything. But to see the looks in their eyes when your granddad gets going, it's pretty clear that they don't know what they don't know."

Now they both laughed, enjoying a joke as can only two AARP members who know that Youth is a flimsy house of cards in desperate need of a foundation that comes only with age.

"Well, I certainly appreciate your candor and understanding, Ms. Anderson. I will go talk to my grandpa right now." He rose, extending his hand to the nurse, excited to feel the soft touch gloved in her firm grip. Louie offered a smile of his own. He strategically extended the handshake to hold her hand as long as possible. "I hope to see you again, but under less…risqué?…circumstances," he said as he turned toward the hallway to the patients' rooms.

Nurse Anderson gently pulled her hand back – subtly enough to not offend, yet slowly enough to still suggest she might like to hold hands again sometime. "Yes, that would be nice, Mr. Jackson," she said.

****

Louie checked each door as he passed until he came to the one bearing his grandfather's name on a postcard-sized label hanging at eye level: "Ronald Gates." He knocked, turned the knob, and announced himself in one swift motion.

"Pop-Pop, it's Louie," he called into the room. "Are you up?"

Ronald Gates emerged from the bathroom trailed by a toilet flush. "Of course, I'm up! It's almost lunchtime, isn't it?" He moved surprisingly fast and smoothly for a man three years shy of a century, a testament to his youthful love for any kind of athletic competition.

110

Louie had watched his maternal grandfather play – and win – many a game of baseball, basketball, tennis, even paintball when Louie had taken up the then-trendy activity in the 1980s. Mr. Gates closed the gap quickly and wrapped his still-strong arms around his oldest grandchild.

"To what do I owe the pleasure today, Louis?" He'd always called Louie by his full name.

"Oh, nothing special." Louie looked out the window, hoping his grandfather wouldn't see the lie on his face. "Just thought I'd stop by, check in on you, make sure you've got everything you need."

"That's very thoughtful of you," Gates said. "Maybe that's why you're my favorite grandson!" He smiled and flicked a light jab into Louie's ribs.

"I'm your only grandson, Pop-Pop!"

"Ok, but still, you should never refuse a compliment, young man. You never know if you'll ever get any more."

Or, if I might ever get a date with that hot nurse…the thought was incongruous, but Louie used it as a springboard to leap to the real purpose for his visit.

"Pop-Pop when I came in, I happened to see your nurse, Ms. Anderson –"

"Oh, she's attractive, isn't she? If I weren't old enough to be her father…"

"Well, grandfather, actually, I think…" Louie said. "But in any case, yes, her. And she mentioned something that concerns me just a bit." Louie shuffled over to the overstuffed, plush, Brady Bunch green couch along the wall facing the television. Ratty along the arms, the start of a tear in one cushion, it was nothing that he'd ever buy, but it came with the room. "Come sit down."

The old man joined his fifty-two-year-old grandson on the couch. "What can I do you for, Louis?"

Louie chuckled. His grandfather's witticisms anchored and defined an irrefutable charm that endeared him to nearly everyone.

"Well, to be honest, the nurse, Ms. Anderson, told me that you've been talking a lot recently about your sex life to the patients and staff, and it's upsetting some of them."

"Really?" Gates said. "I can honestly say I don't remember doing that, but if you say so…what exactly have I been telling them?"

"Lots of things, but the one that came up the most, I guess, is about your first time making love – I assume with Grandma."
Ronald's right hand cupped his chin, rubbing the stubble of unshaven beard. "No, that can't be right, because your grandmother wasn't my first."

Louie inhaled sharply at this revelation.

"Oh, Louis, don't act so surprised," Ronald tut-tutted. "Your generation didn't invent pre-marital sex. I had two partners before your grandmother. The first, like most 'Firsts' of just about anything, wasn't very good. I was no expert either if I'm honest. But the experience itself changed my world."

Louie flopped back into the giant couch cushion. He felt like he would never stop sinking, so he grabbed the arm of the couch with his left hand to stabilize himself.

"You know what the best part was?" Ronald smiled at the memory forming where memories were now so very scarce.

"I don't really want to…"

"It wasn't the act itself. No, that went very quickly and didn't do much for either of us, truth be told," Ronald said. "No sir, it was when she raised her hips from her parent's bed – they were out for the night and never thought twice about leaving her alone with me she raised her hips and let me pull down her underwear. I mean to tell you, there is absolutely nothing more meaningful or sacred to a man as when the woman he loves, or at least, lusts for, willingly gives herself over. The intimacy of that act, the faith, the commitment, the trust, the confidence, the air of control, that's what makes it so sexy and powerful." Ronald paused, drew a deep breath. "And magical. I'll remember that forever, dementia or not."

Louie's heart raced like a stallion out of the gate. The air crashed out of his lungs as if he'd just been hit with a medicine ball. "Pop-Pop!"

"What?" Ronald said, voicing a mixture of sincere exasperation and surprise. "You mean to tell me that's never happened to you? I mean, I know you've been single your whole life, but I assume you've been with a woman or two?"

Of course, his grandfather was right. Louie'd never been especially lucky in the love department, but he'd been around the sexual block a few times. Enough to know the exact thrill of which his ninety-seven-year-old Pop-Pop spoke.

"Well, the first time for me was actually kind of similar," he confessed. "I was a freshman in high school, on a band trip to Canada for a competition and sitting on the seat next to one of the flag girls. We'd been kinda-sorta flirting for a while, nothing too serious. But it was a long, long, loooonnngg drive. It was night. There was a blanket covering our laps. We were holding hands under the blanket when she suddenly guided my hand down the inside of the front of her pants which, somehow, she'd unbuttoned and unzipped. My fingers touched her, you know, down there. I didn't know much, but I knew enough, and I did what I knew. She didn't stop me from touching her, but she refused to touch me for some reason."

Louie laughed at a sudden "Aha!" moment. "I guess I was just her love slave for that night!" He paused, eyes closed, savoring the movie running through his brain, then snapped back to attention. "But Pop-Pop, that's not the point."

"Oh? Pleasuring someone is not the point?"

"Well, I mean, it was the point at that time, but not right now. The point now, is, you can't be sharing your memories and stories with people here. It's shocking to hear that kind of stuff from a man of your..."

"My what? My age?"

"Well, yes."

Ronald stood again and paced toward the television then back to the couch. He extended his right hand to his grandson. "Louis Jackson, I love you, but I am terribly disappointed in you."

"What?" Louie was both confused and surprised. "Disappointed in me? What did I do?"

"It's not what you did, but what you didn't do. You didn't defend me."

"Pop-Pop, I don't understand."

"No, apparently not. So let me help." Ronald said. He pulled his grandson close, rubbed his left cheek, then put both hands on either side of Louie's head.

"I am here because I have dementia. I know this as well as anyone. I know that every day I have one less joke to tell, one less bit of wisdom to teach, one less story to share. I lose one more part of me."

Louie raised his right hand to his face and wiped away the start of a tear. "I know that Pop-Pop, I know, but…"

"No but's!" Ronald barked loudly. He released Louie's face and waved his right hand in the air. "God forbid you should ever know this pain, but in the meantime, I need you to know about it, so you can at least explain. I don't mean to offend or hurt anyone's feelings. I am just trying to be Me as long as I can."

Ronald grabbed his grandson again and kissed him on the cheek and forehead as if Louie was a baby. "Who I am, is who I was. And I am losing who I was. So, I am sharing whatever is left of me while I still can. If that happens to be a dirty story, well, I am truly sorry if I accidentally offend someone, but if I do, you just tell them: it could be worse."

"How could it be worse, Pop-Pop?" Louie knew the second the question cleared his lips – and from the wide grin on Ronald's face - that his grandfather, ever the jokester, ever the performer, had set him up, dementia be damned.

"I could have crapped in the potted plants, like Old Man Carbondale!"

THE GAME OF MY LIFE

By Ed Calkins

From the BryonySeries novel "Ruthless" by Edward Calkins

Even as a ruthless vampire unable to remember who, where, and why, I can never forget the game of my life.

Time was running out as I scanned the opposition's defenses. Sweat from my eyes dribbled down my face. With a little more than a minute left on the clock, I tried to keep my poise. Before the game started, a loss of this type seemed unthinkable, but there it was, with only seconds separating winner from loser, and the rest of my life in the balance. It was all on me to find an eligible man deep and uncovered, but I still had to deliver victory. No other options were present. I was tactically overmatched, and time pressure forbade any other chance for a win. Sure, many other fifteen-year old boys must have felt this same pressure, except this game really was the one to set the tone for the rest of my life. There would be no second chance, no redemption, no forgetting.

I made my move. Out of the corner of my eye, I saw what I dreaded. A red flag rose. I knew if it fell, I'd wonder for the rest of my life what might have been if I only did this game differently. A strange thought came to me. Fighting the daze of fatigue, I reached within my soul to put out better than I ever was.

Why was I doing this? What was it that made this game so important?

Remember now, I was fifteen, so there really was only one possible answer. Why does any teenage boy give his all? Teenage girls! I was no different, except I was willing to work for it. I knew that an average effort towards football wouldn't get me noticed. Two hundred other boys tried out for freshman football, and nearly all of them were faster, stronger, and heavier than I was. I knew my efforts had to be superhuman. Before the first tryouts, I had already put myself into training. Every morning before my paper route, I'd wake up an hour early and do pushups till I could do them no more. Then I'd do sit ups, pull ups, and jumping jacks, same way. After the route, I'd put away my bike and run until – you guessed it – until I could run no more.

Tryouts could have gotten me discouraged. By the way, since coaches knew the better candidates by name, I understood that many of the boys felt they'd already decided who'd made the team. In this private, Catholic school, many of the chosen had been given a full ride, saving $500 per year on tuition. I had to work part-time to earn even that, as my single parent home couldn't afford the expense, nor were my grades sufficient enough to earn such a ride. I did have a "poor boy" scholarship, which I suspected Fr. John Chokey had arranged, but that only cut the tuition in half. I had to earn the rest or attend an inferior public school.

"Winners never quit, and quitters never win!"

I heard that and other inspirational messages at least ten times during each tryout/practice. Every day for a month, fewer and fewer boys came out. Then school started and even fewer boys came out, with even fewer placed on the team roster. But football games aren't won by sitting on the bench. I fought hard, worked with uncomplaining relentlessness, and stayed committed to getting a spot as a starter. By midseason, it was clear that, despite my devotion, I was too slow, weak, and small to actually play for the school. My freshman season ended without me on the playing field for a single snap.

I was also having problems with grades. That was nothing new to me. I struggled all through my schooling career, although I'd managed to qualify for a top high school and even a top college. Nobody really understood dyslexia then, and I wasn't diagnosed till my last year in college. I tried hard, or I didn't try at all, depending on perspective of teacher or student. Still, my grades left me eligible to try out for varsity my sophomore year. So I threw myself into spring training with a vigor that was viewed as comical, even by some of the less sensitive coaches. 'Let them laugh,' I told myself. I'll find a leadership role on this team and pull us all to victory.

I had plenty to be discouraged about my sophomore year. The team did well, but once again I never got on the playing field; in fact, I never dressed for the game. While they had sixty complete football gear for practices, they only had fifty-five game jerseys, and

I was one of the five who was on the team every day but game day. Still I hung tough and didn't quit. Of that five, I was the only one that tried out again as a junior.

My junior year was a breakout year for the name "Calkins." Though the season ended with a playoff loss, the best offense center in the league was Calkins, but not Ed Calkins. My cousin Larry held that honor for that season and the next. He would go on to win a full ride to an ivy league university. I don't mean to dismiss my contributions to the team for I had found a role for myself. You might have heard of the joke: I play guard, tackle and end...coach told me to sit at the end of the bench, guard the water bucket, and tackle anyone that comes near it." Heard that one? No, I wasn't even good enough for the bench. As in the previous the year, I was only on the team during practice where I found my true calling... blocking dummy.

Though I was only one hundred and forty pounds in a downpour, I was the right height to give real football players a surface to practice hitting. Better than that, I never quit, which was quite annoying to blockers, thus fueling a better effort. And, too, my obligatory grunts were so high pitched, they irritated the blockers' ears and, thus, inspired greater force.

So football never got me noticed, expect for ridicule, even though I gave football everything I ever had. My athletic career, like my academic career, was something I survived and I'm proud of that much, but it never gave me a sense of manliness or a well-paying job. It did, however, teach me lessons of value. On the football field, I learned that everyone, no matter how small or physically flawed, is tougher than me so if I didn't want to look foolish, I'd better act respectful lest I get my butt kicked by a midget - or even a girl. School taught me that no matter how much I learned, how much I studied, or how much I knew, anyone who listened to me or read anything that I wrote would assume they were smarter than me. So I learned to get the thing I wanted out of life by acting stupid.

I also did learn to take pleasure in doing hard work. Because of that alone, I am luckier than most.

During my high school years, other important things were going on in the world. In Vietnam, the United States was losing its first war, which was unthinkable a decade earlier. Hippies still refused to cut their hair, and Catholics started living in sin, rather than getting married. With all this corruption, coupled with a president resigning and the sexual revolution breaking out of bedrooms everywhere, someone, mainly Catholic teenage boys, had to fight back. We heard one message everywhere we went. It was our moral responsibility to never believe the crazy notion the times were changing and that all was right with God and the USA.

We were told long hair on boys was unnatural, disgusting, immoral, and made young men cowards. They felt only short haired boys too young to get drafted would lie about their age for God and country. Corruption? Forget about Watergate. The real corruption was easy to spot in any man's hairline that didn't reveal ears. Hair that covered ears, that's where the devil speaks…and the woman with him? She's probably on the pill instead of making babies like she's supposed to. Together, they were the reason people had to pay taxes, not to kill Charlie, but to support marijuana farms in crazy sex-filled commie communes where nobody married anybody.

Then there was the sexual revolution. Now, I've heard of the double standard that might have existed around the country, if not the world, but in our all-male Catholic high school, we were lectured daily on the perils of damnation for having sex before marriage. Not that we were encouraged to get married. Marriage was a bad thing, but it was survivable if you prayed a lot and worked hard. After all, not every man had the stuff to become a priest. But if you're going to be weak and go for marriage, avoid the eternal fires and get some priest to marry you. At least that way, your suffering will come to an end when you die.

One of the Dominican brothers that taught was more vulgar than most in his lectures.

"Remember that every date with your girlfriend is a fight for your soul," he told us. "You know in your head that anything you could do with her isn't worth burning forever in hell, but your little head (yes, he'd actually point to his crotch) doesn't. It's a battle between the big head and the little head. Yes, if you go down that way, you can be forgiven, but you're much more likely to blow off salvation altogether. How many of those hippies do you think go to

118

confession? Remember that. Unfortunately, some of you will only remember that in hell."

Of course, I was a nerd, so damnation by the traditional "date with girlfriend" route was kind of slim. My plan to win damnation was as simple as it was ruthless, with a touch of elegance that bordered on genius, even though the objects of my affection swore it would never work. My method for carnal knowledge? Being the last man on earth. No, I wasn't going to play mad scientist and kill every other man on the planet; that idea lacked elegance. I was going to wait for some less nerdier nerds to have the same thought and start killing the other guys while I hid, waiting for the numbers to go down. Then I'd spring out and kill the last surviving killer. The plan might seem extreme to you but having every woman or girl on earth seemed like fair compensation to me. I also envisioned less extreme versions of the plan; I could be the last man in the state, zip code, or village. That would work, although it would create an American postal bride wave. Or I could be the last single man in the world, country, state, zip code, or village. Maybe I'd have to settle for being the last man that some bad girl never had. I might have to settle for that. But in either case, it involved a lot of waiting things out.

Then there was the biggest conflict of all. The commies. Yes, the cold war was in full swing, and although my age group was just a little too young for the draft, we still had to fight the bigger picture. With a remorseful apology to Vietnam vets, I have to admit that my age group was told that "Nam" was a little war compared to what we'd see if we didn't stem the flow of communism. That's how truly evil communism was. Sin could take us to hell when we died, but commies would make sure we didn't have to wait.

On that front, we didn't have lot of good news, but we did have Bobby Fischer. Except for a few nerds, everyone knew that chess was a commie game that no real American would bother to learn. Some even felt the game itself was a communist plot. Nevertheless, the year 1972 saw the greatest chess players in the world square off with Fischer representing the Free World and Spassky representing the Godless communists. This time Godly won, crushing the way for this ill-charmed contentious man to be the media sweetheart of the free world.

Quite suddenly, everyone in America started playing chess. In bars and hangouts where the incoherent used to argue politics, religion, and philosophy, they now argued chess theories and, in some cases, even played the game.

My remarkable opportunity came with an unlikely invitation to a teenage party. I should note that this might not be as unlikely as it seemed, as the party was sponsored by an adult group, which marked it as a party for the unattractive or socially inept. Parties that cool kids went to were mostly "goodbye" parties for parents leaving for somewhere, usually vacations, trusting their teenage children would behave sanely and not do anything rash, like throw a party. Parents of that era were experts at misplaced trust.

Misplaced trust could have been the buzz phase to describe the 70s, as pedophiles seemed to lurk around every trusted institution where children or underaged teens were served. The abuse of Churches is well-known today, but back then a child could find molestation by pediatricians, nurses, child psychiatrists or psychologist, carnival workers, juvenile case workers, crossing guards, daycare workers, teen club moderators, and parents. Anywhere children were, so were pedophiles, and no one ever seemed to catch on.

We didn't know it then; it wasn't a party talking point even for the socially awkward, but everyone in this teen club was molested by someone from the above occupations at some earlier time. Though a different definition was assigned to this club, Trudy, a girl my age whom I met at Wraith Park, suggested that I, coming from a single parent home, qualified as a member and could attend the party as one of her guests.

Luck favored me. Among broken teens, I was less likely to stand out. By now, it was the September of 1973 and I arrived late to the party as I had football practice, a fact I hoped to use to impress some gullible girl. I never got the chance to mention that. In fact, I never got a chance to introduce myself as the party was dominated by a chess board, where Trudy was proving her intellectual

120

superiority over her new twenty-something boyfriend by beating him.

Knowledge of chess was mostly required of nerds back then in that there was no Klingon language to learn yet, and "Dungeons and Dragons" had yet to spawn. True, there was Star Trek and the "Trekkies" that worshiped it, but Star Wars had yet to debut; so true nerds had only chess, philosophy, or homework to replace our lack of companionship.

"Do you know how to play?" Trudy asked, seeing me sitting there, looking out of place. I could play winner, if I wanted, but there were three others before me. I waited. It wasn't like me to keep my mouth shut, but I already realized that anything that came out of my mouth would make me less attractive to the girls, who were in equal number with the boys. So I endured the running uninformed commentaries of the next three games, hoping for my chance.

Yes, I played chess. Before high school, I was the best player I knew. My dad taught me the game because he was bored with the other "family" games he felt required to play with my siblings and me as proof that he did more than drink all the time. Monopoly was too long, checkers too boring, and we kids didn't have enough money for poker. In a couple years, I excelled in the game and could beat my dad, so he quit playing, claiming it was the game that drove him to drink. With no one to play against, I played myself, turning the board after every move.

It was after football practice finished late one evening, and I discovered I needed a book from my school locker, that I heard chess pieces moving in one of the classrooms. Investigating, I discovered that my high school had a chess team I could try out for. Of course, this was out of the question, as all the matches coincided with freshman football, but there was also a club, and anyone could play. I played three games on the spot with team candidates, losing each one. Still, I was evenly matched enough to get instruction on how to improve and how to read chess notation so I could review that games I played.

By the time of this party, I had gotten better, sometimes beating the players that had made the team. Because I could only play after football practice, I was playing only the players that practiced the hardest, or at least the longest.

When it came to my turn at the party, Trudy still held the board, having beaten the other three players. I knew by then that I could easily take her apart and did just that with a "Scholar's mate" in three moves. After that, I found myself still playing Trudy, but really the whole party, as kibitzing replaced any conversation.

By the fourth game, I was really feeling good. While the games could have bored me to tears, I was the focus of a party and not through ridicule!

I was being set up for a knockdown.

"He's really good," Trudy remarked as her loyal followers marveled. "But I don't think he could beat Malcolm." Then looking at me she asked. "How many players in your school can say they never lost a game...ever?

I knew I wasn't a very good liar, so I admitted that I didn't know anyone who never lost. Unable to keep silent, I admitted that I lost about one third of my games against chess team members and drew still another third. Surely, this Malcolm didn't win every game he played; draws were the most common results in high level play. But no, Trudy claimed he won every game he ever played.

Not everyone agreed with Trudy. One of the girls pointed out that I had beaten her quicker than Malcolm had. Apparently, he liked to play with his food, removing pieces one by one like pulling the wings and legs off a fly. I always went for the kill, checkmating where I could with all the pieces on the board.

"Maybe I could play him," I suggested. "That way we could know."

That way, too, I'd get invited to another party with girls in it.

But I was not invited to the next party. I found out because my mother had joined the adult club that had spawned the teen club. She was having trouble meeting single men who properly justified her loathing for the gender. This club was perfect for her. My exclusion was explained by the host's parents not knowing me and the fact that it fell on one of the teen's birthday.

The next party was different. Trudy called me herself, informing me that Malcolm was coming and bringing his chess clock. I'd never played with a chess clock, but I had a week to prepare. The high school chess team did use chess clocks, and after explaining the importance of the game to be played, the boys were willing to coach me.

Now Trudy was not a beautiful girl, but she had a directness that fed into her charismatic sex appeal. At a time when teenage girls were divided into the ones that did and the ones that did not, having a girlfriend was no guarantee of more than a peck on the cheek lest boys not respect her. There were good girls and easy girls, with none wanting to be the latter. Trudy broke the mold. No teenage boy could call her easy, because to teenage boys, she was completely unavailable. Neither was she a good girl; she was the prototype of the selectively promiscuous attitude that would come to her peers a decade later. I was expecting to score not with her but with the boy-crazy girls that orbited around her because they were unable to navigate the slut/princess mentality of the day. I didn't have to explain all of that to the chess club. They understood perfectly when I told them there were girls at the party.

The week passed quickly, and I went to the address ready to play chess, but there was a change of plans. The party was in the basement. That alone wasn't enough to change anything, but the teen club moderator was upstairs drinking with the host's mom.

"Not now." Trudy said to Malcolm, pointing to his chess clock. "We may never get a chance like this, so this is a make out party."

Everyone liked the sound of that, but no one except Trudy seemed to know what a make out party was. Simple! Pair up, shut off lights, and make out. Trudy's boyfriend wasn't present, so she pointed at a guy and then at a couch. Something like, "You! There." Each of the remaining girls were to do the same thing. Giggling or blushing, each girl complied. But of course, there were three more guys than girls, so Malcolm, I, and someone else went unselected and bore the duty of lookout.

What could we do? It was too dark to play chess and we didn't want to sound rude. Someday there would be both a make out party and enough girls to go around. What else could we talk about? Only three things interested me; girls, football, and chess. I didn't know much about girls, and Malcolm didn't care about football. For the first three minutes, we waited for the third guy to start us off. It took us that long to realize he had left.

So we discussed the Fischer-Spassky match down to some of the chess notated moves, which might have convinced Malcolm that I would be worth beating. He felt that Spassky was the better player, but Fischer had gotten in his head. I felt that Fischer had gotten in his own head but was the better player.

While listening to the soundtrack of teenagers making out, chess wasn't going to carry the party. Malcolm admitted he was hurt, but not surprised that he was not chosen, while I admitted to being only frustrated. Which girl did we want? Both would have been happy with any, but Trudy was our first choice, as it was sure with her that there would be some running of bases…even if she did the running. The fact was, neither of us had ever kissed a girl, but Malcolm was confident that future make-out parties might have enough, or more, girls than boys. He figured if he just stuck around longer and was better known, he would be better liked and not last all the time. We seemed to share a mild version that of "last man alive" plan.

He wasn't there the day that the conditions for such a party included one extra girl, so Trudy offered to share her choice with the unpaired girl. The lucky guy didn't say much, partly because as Trudy's boyfriend he was neither a teen nor a virgin, but it's rumored all bases were skipped, and the party of three went oral.

In my time as a teen, to get close to that far with a girl, you had to have a car. None of the teens in the club had a car, but we had Trudy.

The party ended quickly with a smashing bottle and some yelling from upstairs. The parents, who were supposed to be chaperoning the party were also having an affair, but now they were fighting. Kids took their cue and ditched the place through the basement door, even the daughter of the mother hosting the party.

Trudy apologized to both of us once we were outside. If there were only one of us, she'd have let us share her, but four boys and one girl was too hard to do, and boys tended to get all inhibited with having to share anyway.

124

The next three parties were not nearly as enticing, but by then my mother had joined the club, so I became a member of the teen club and not just a guest. Her joining was predictable even though I had the good sense not to tell her about the club. She, while looking for a husband, loathed men in general. She cited them as morally weak and repeatedly found those men who could support her theory. Most of the male parents kept very loose or no contacts with their own kids and thus were free to screw up somebody else's.

Still, teen parties were scheduled monthly, and each one seemed an opportunity to make out or play chess against the undefeated Malcolm. But fall had turned to winter, and winter to spring; thus like the melting snow, interest in chess waned. No longer was chess a center of activity. That gave way to listening to four guys practice their 'air' instruments to the radio. We were to believe they were a band, though none of the had musical instruments, let alone ability to play them.

The game wasn't going to happen at any party, but it was definitely going to happen. Though chess lost its relevance, the debate on who was smarter continued. While Trudy and her followers stuck by Malcolm, some of the boys, who must have viewed me as less of a rival for the girls in the club, sided with me. The way the guys were acting, it almost confirmed what I suspected. Even though this group was a collection of the socially undesired, there was a pecking order which allowed for only one smart kid. As far as academic achievement, the collection already had an 'A' student, Debbie, so the 'brain' slot was taken. Two chess geniuses would have to narrow to one.

On the fourth party, Trudy had enough. The talk had to stop and the knowable had to be made known. The Malcolm and Eddie match would be held at her house on a Sunday afternoon, as it wouldn't affect my football practice or Malcolm's marching band. The date and time were set. Wagers were made and anyone who wished to watch the game was invited.

At some point that day, Malcolm and I made a wager…one we'd never admit to anyone. The stakes were already as high as they could get, but with this wager…Malcolm must have been confident of victory. I had little to lose except this chance.

125

I got there on time, but I could have believed I was early. Outside of Malcolm sitting in front of a set up board and his chess clock aside, no one was there but Trudy and her curious mother, who disbelieved that her daughter was hosting a game of chess that she was going to watch.

I felt the blood rushing through my veins, but I tried to act confident with the obvious question and its heavy pull. Which seat was mine…that is: would I play the black pieces or the white? White had an advantage.

Malcolm was fair. Solemnly, he grabbed a white pawn in one hand and a black pawn in the other, then placed the hands behind his back where he could mix them, then held both closed fists out.

"Pick one."

I picked black, not a true disaster. If I were able to pull out a draw, Trudy might suspect me as the better player or at least declare another game with me as white. Malcolm set the clocks. A chess clock is a simple thing: two faces, one for each player, with an hour and minute hand and a button above each face. When a player made his move, he would press the button above his own, stopping his clock and starting the other. The most intimidating feature was the two red flaps, or flags, situated to the minute hand, which would lift the flap up at one minute to midnight. If that flag dropped before a win or draw was achieved, that player simply lost.

I was sweating a little…I always sweated as I had over-developed underarms. But so was Malcolm. Trudy's mother noticed the seriousness we players were radiating. She had to ask.

"You're not playing for money, are you?"

Both of our hearts must have skipped a beat. If she knew what we were actually playing for…

Malcolm recovered with a joke.

"No, we're playing for your daughter's hand.'

Trudy's mother laughed and then monologued about how she would be proud to have either one of us as Trudy's husband or boyfriend. Her continuing praise of our collective upstanding virtues was "parent speak" that we were too nerdy to score any sexual advances with her daughter. The game began while she was still talking. Malcolm started his clock, made his move, started mine, and

126

scribbled its notation on the paper beside him as we were both recording this game. Trudy wanted to crawl under the table.

Now, if you're not a chess nut, there's probably nothing more boring than watching to guys go into deep thought over a chess game. We each had forty minutes on our clock, the high school chess matches' norm, so although we'd have to conserve our mulling over potential moves, we had plenty of time to bore any bystanders. Worse than that, we played a textbook opening called the "giuoco piano," which means "peaceful game" in Italian, but boring, boring, boring to casual chess observers.

Trudy's mom left when she realized no one was listening to her. Trudy tried to stay interested, but she expected to keep appraised of who was winning by the value of the pieces captured. She couldn't take it either and disappeared into her room.

Almost as soon as she left, pieces started flying of the board.

I know that it's a bad idea to write about the moves in the game, but I've been studying this one game all my life. I wouldn't be the nerd I am if I didn't want to give you each chess notated move, complete with analysis and commentary. While I can skip that, I simply must get off my chest what happened on the board in the biggest game of my life.

As if reading for a textbook, the predictable pieces left the board without any real advantage to either. Two center pawns apiece, black squared bishops, knight for knight, exchange evenly giving me hope that if I could keep exchange, it would end in a draw. Later, an exchange of my knight for his bishop but doubled my Queen's bishop's pawn gave him a slight strategic advantage and me a slight tactical one. With our centers squares vacated, we both castled king side.

Then came the move. It was the only conversation in the game. While this game had no master strokes or obvious blunders, it did have a defining move, and this was it. I would never make the same move in the hundreds of recorded games that I would play before leaving high school. Still, on this day I would chew up nearly ten minutes of my clock trying to talk myself out of it. The move I was contemplating was both elegant and tragic with a sense of romanticized melancholy. Then, with a dramatic flair, my red bishop took his unprotected queen's rook's pawn.

Shocked, hurt, and maybe outraged at my boldness, he looked up at me but responded first, completely reasonably, with pawn to queen's knight three effectively sealing off my bishop from play.

"Did you forget?" he asked me gently.

I shook my head. I hadn't forgotten. No. I made my move as deliberately as the statement I was making by it, a sad statement, though bold.

You see, the move I made under, as far as we could tell, almost identical positions, was the same move that Fischer made in that first game vs Spassky. Everyone concluded, including Malcolm and I, that move was the blunder that cost America that first game against the Russian world champion. What was I saying here? Was I trying to get into Malcolm's head? Was I trying to undermine his confidence? Or was I in my own head and just being sad?

There was some logic to my move. Malcolm was about to mount an attack on my king side, using all his major pieces and threating checkmate. My bishop, though out of play, would cost him two precious moves to claim my bishop for two pawns, diverting at least a rook away from his attack and give me a chance to improve my defense.

But Malcolm would have none of it. He ignored a bishop that would never see play. With brute force, he doubled his queen and rook, while advancing his knight, keeping me in constant peril of making a fatal mistake. I was able to trade queens, then rooks, but that knight kept checking me, trying to fork my pawns. I'm not sure if he saw this right away, or later when I did, but he had to keep checking me, lest I advance my doubled pawn, forcing an exchange that would free my bishop.

Trying to dance with his knight, I committed my last rook to my king's defense which forced a hard decision for my opponent. He could trade our last rooks and take a two-pawn advantage, but I'd get my bishop back if he left me two free moves. The exchange happened.

Realizing that I was unable to defend my king, I raced my king to the toward the center of the board. With my red bishop still on the board, the game was now a chase, him up in pieces, but one move short of queening a pawn first. If there was any way for Malcolm to reverse the game or get a draw at this point, he never found it, nor did I upon many replaying and reliving this victory. My 25th move would be my last.

Malcolm toppled his king.

For what he lost that day, Malcolm was a true gentleman. He didn't swipe the pieces of the board, cry foul in some way, or try to make excuses as I might have done in my immaturity. I, for my part, managed to mask my elation. I offered my hand, telling him that it was a good game and that he'd played it well. He shook my hand, though he must have been dying inside. Still, he had to leave right away. He had just remembered he was supposed to do something.

Trudy must have heard the rustling of coats. Who was leaving without even saying goodbye?

Running down the stairs, she caught him at the door with coat on and chess clock under his arm.

Confused she asked the obvious question. "Who won?"

"He did," Malcolm admitted, waiting for a comment.

I've found in life that just because somebody lost, it doesn't mean his rival won. That would have been the case only if Trudy had looked at him sideways. Such a look would mean, "I thought you were good. How could you have never lost a game if the first guy I put on you beat you?" But Trudy didn't do that. Instead she gave me that sideways glance. With nothing to explain, Malcolm left. I don't doubt it was to cry in his pillow as I would had done.

"Why didn't you tell me you're that smart?' she challenged me the moment Malcolm was not among us.

I saw the gambit. I could have explained that my high school had an extremely proficient chess team and that my being able to handle them on equal terms qualified me as a future grandmaster. Maybe she'd never know otherwise. Maybe I could believe the same and convince myself that I was the next Bobby Fischer. But I would have to defend that lie.

The truth is often a buzzkill, but it's the most powerful piece of anyone's mind, if you develop it. I told her what I had just finished telling Malcolm with my bishop takes queen's rook's pawn. I wasn't that smart, and neither was Malcolm. We were just two guys with nothing more enjoyable to do then study chess after our homework was done. Neither one of us would ever be grandmaster no matter how hard we played, studied, and practiced. We were good, maybe better than a hundred random teens who knew the game. Maybe, if we kept playing and tried really hard, we'd be better than a random thousand, but to ever get national notice, we'd need to be better than millions. There were too many guys like us that couldn't get girlfriends. One in a hundred thousand was bound to have a photographic memory and never have to study a losing position a second time.

She resisted at first, pointing out the things the Malcolm could do in chess, like playing and winning without seeing the board or playing several games at once and winning them all. I could do those things as well. A lot of boys could if they played on a team.

The board was still as it was when the white king fell. I offered to replay the game for her, complete with my analyses. She declined, disappointing me, but not surprising. She told me to leave; that she wanted to be alone. All I could think was that I somehow blew it with a girl again, and I gathered my coat. The exit out was not three yards from the table where the game was played. Trudy sat in Malcolm's seat and touched the downed white king.

She started getting teary eyed.

I was wondering how much she bet on the game, but of course, I was on the wrong track. Looking back at me, she explained with anger in her voice.

"We're a bunch of oddballs in this group, all for different reasons. We're a group of outcasts that no other group with take, but I always hoped for some kind of justice…like maybe someone would prove to be so good at something that everyone else that ignored or mocked us would be forced to turn around and take notice."

Yeah! That was it! Every nerd that ever lived must have felt that way. Wait till that ray gun gets invented that kills all the cool guys.

"There's always football."

"You're too small, too slow, and too weak. Guys that lift nothing more than beer cans are stronger than you," she responded coldly. "You'd have a better chance getting noticed for chess."

"Did I get noticed by you?"

It was the question I had as I walked out the door. I don't remember if I actually asked her, but she did answer the next day when she called me for the first time just to talk. Mostly, she apologized for taking her disappointment out on me. Yes, she did lose a bet, and someone was going to get head this month.

I'm quite sure that I haven't explained it yet, why winning that game was so important and how it changed the course of my teenage years. Maybe, I'm making too much of it, or the grandeur of defeating Malcolm grows in my mind with its retelling. I really don't think so.

Let me explain it this way, though I think it's something more. Maybe winning that game and having this small group know about it gave me just a little more confidence and Malcolm the reverse. Maybe all the stupid or inappropriate things I said were now taken with that "He beat Malcolm in chess" grain of salt. I started to feel like I belonged to this group. While Malcolm still came to teen club functions, he faded somewhat.

Trudy was out of my league and would stay so well into my 20s, but we did become friends. Trudy wasn't just the first girl that was nice to me; she was the first friend that was nice to me. I won the right to hang around and that worked the way I hoped it would, getting chance after chance with the girls that clung to her.

There were other make out parties...five in all before the teen club's demise. At that point there were eight core members, five guys and three girls. I sat out again for three of those parties but the last two...well, that's when I kissed my first girl.

The teen club was doomed, however, and would only last ten more months. At the start of my sophomore year, a mystery was solved about Tammy. She was quite attractive if she didn't pick her nose, but she never spoke. Strangely, she was always the first to be picked up and the last to be dropped off during teen club functions. It turns out the teen club moderator, the same guy having an affair with Debbie's mother, was doing her. The resulting scandal was enough to call the adult members into action. Being the rational parents of the 70s, they defined the problem and got rid of the teen club. How else were the forty-somethings going to compete for the men in the group if the fourteen-year old sluts were there to take all the men away?

The result was that the fewer teens met more often, and I made the cut. By that time, I wasn't just Trudy's friend, I was her best friend. Although that wasn't getting me in Trudy's pants, it was giving me contact with other girls who were less desirable but far better than nothing. Dates were few, and none led to anything, but it did give me just a little more confidence. By the time I hit twenty-one, I lived with a girl that Trudy hand-picked for me. I lost my virginity and became an expectant father on the same night, and it seemed to me that my life was going exactly as my detractors expected it would.

It turns out, we were wrong.

I stayed with the mother until she found another less nerdy guy, but I kept support and contact with my son. The relationship lasted just long enough for me to learn about being a boyfriend and father, which almost had me scrapping the "last man on earth" plan. Winning that game was the only thing the big head ever did for the little head. Or maybe it's the reveres.

Then I met my lover for life. At first, it seemed to me that, although I was physically attracted to her, she was on track to "friend zone" me, which is a great phase to describe so many relationships I had but the term didn't exist back then. Maybe again, it was that little extra confidence that let me slightly push for something more…slightly being the operative word that might be replaceable by nerdy.

I realize that if I end this tale here, I would leave out three important elements unexplained; what was with the beginning about the red flag dropping, why did I refer to chess notation but didn't use it, and what was the bet that me and Malcolm had.

132

As to the first, look, I'm writing about chess. It would have been hard for me to draw you in without as much drama as possible. It's not that the game didn't happen, just that it wasn't as important. That game would happen two years later, when I was a much better player. As a junior, I would be co-captain of the chess team that played the last round in the state tournament. All other game were finished back then, and the opposition had just locked in first place. Our team would finish second if I won, third if I drew, and fourth if I lost.

I lost.

With not enough time on the clock, I made too many mistakes on the board and toppled my king before the red flag fell. I was too inexperienced compared to my opponent and had to find over the board answers to positions he had previously encountered.

I still had a lot to be proud of. Not playing throughout the chess season because it conflicted with football made my making the tournament very unlikely. Further still, the chess team was under .500 in the regular matches, so qualifying against the teams that had beaten the team that didn't include me made me feel impressive. Of five games in the semi-finals, I won three, lost one, and drew one. In the eight game finals, I won four, lost two, and drew two. Impressive as it was, it didn't seem as important as the one game match with Malcolm.

Once back home, I learned just how unimportant the downstate tournament was. Though the fourth-place finish did make the opening announcements, no one from outside the chess club ever congratulated us. More the that, when I was reunited with my father, who I hadn't seen for six years, I excitedly told him about the downstate showdown. He thought for a moment then answered, "I guess that's O.K., as long as it doesn't take any of your attention away from football."

It was then I realized that girls were not the reason for either game, I was trying to impress my father. My senior year would be the worst year of my life, which my former coach kept pointing out. He claimed that I'd become a quitter. I didn't go to the same school or play football or chess. Looking back, I'm surprised I didn't take my own life, but I had Trudy. I didn't need chess anymore; she and

I had discovered poetry. Both from reading and writing, we learned a lot about triumph, despair, loss, love, and how not to seduce women.

From that bad year comes a simple fact that makes me think I'm the luckiest man in the world. I don't have to kill every other male, because since then, every year of my life has been a little better than the last, without exception.

So, who's the loser now, coach?

Which brings us to the chess notation thing. If I know chess notation, why did I write "Bishop takes queen's rook's pawn" instead of "bishop to H2" or the like. If you didn't play chess back in the 70's, you might not know that chess notation used to be like that. Since then (not sure when), the Chess Federation simplified it. Before, each move was described by the file of the major piece that was there in setting up the board, and the rank from the perspective of the mover. I found that very easy. Now, the files are described by the alphabetic order, left to right by white's perspective, and the ranks are also by white's perspective, no matter who moves.

I'm incapable of learning the new way. I could master the ranks, but I never learn the alphabet. While I know all the letters, I could never place them in order. I know what you're going to say. Learn the song. It doesn't help. I know the melody, but like any songs I sing, I keep mixing up the lyrics. If there's only the first three as in "abc," I can do that. I also know "xyz," but anything in the middle is a problem for me. All my life, I've lived in fear of going to a job interview and being asked to recite the alphabet.

Now comes the last question, one I thought I might be too ashamed to answer as it plays into that, "last man on earth" mentality. Before the game, I went to Malcolm's house to compose a letter with him to Trudy. In that letter, we explained that Trudy's life would never be complete until she married either Malcolm or Eddie. Rather the duel to the death, we both agreed that the groom should be the winner of the first match between the both of us. We typed the letter, and both signed it, then we typed another copy and signed again. The plan was to wait until Trudy had slept with every guy she knew except the both of us. Malcolm told Trudy's mother

134

the truth. We were playing for her daughter's hand - only Trudy didn't know.

Bishop takes queen's rook's pawn is a waiting move both bold and humble. I'd never get carnal knowledge of every woman on the planet that way, but I did find something that merely being the last man alive wouldn't get me: love. While other nerds won their brides by wearing them down, that bishop taught me how to wait them out. Just stay there on the board until someone notices that you haven't gone away and believes that, if you're with her, you never will. My lifetime lover would become my wife, mother to my son, and, in time, grandmother to my granddaughters. Each step of that was a greater joy than the last one. I still get depressed, but it's always about the past when I was younger than nineteen. Yes, I quit playing football and chess, but sometimes I can't quit being that nerdy, lonely kid that wanted every other man on the planet dead. Just as true, I can't seem to quit being husband, dad, and grandpa. If you ever meet me, you might call me happy-go-lucky, as many people have. You might catch me smiling in a quiet moment for no apparent reason and wonder about my mental health. You might worry what I've been up to or why I keep so happy where other men doing better see themselves as failures.

Why? Bishop takes queen's rook's pawn.

Try not to be afraid. I threw away my plans for being the last man alive before I threw away the letter making Trudy my wife, lest someone find it and either rat me out to the authorities or Trudy or use those plans themselves.

So if you're wondering how I expect to survive as a psychotic vampire, remember bishop takes quean's rook's pawn from the other side of the board. Will the would-be prime evil know enough to let his bishop sit? Will he/she/it have the patience to play the peaceful game and not reveal the true prime of its evil intent?

Whether in undead or living life, I count my luck in every situation. Luck isn't a passive thing. It's the recognition, post-mortem, of how well you've lived by the luck you've been granted. The bishop will move, and I'll be ready, if only by strange unlikely coincidence.

THE HEAVIEST BURDEN

By Tom Hernandez

A few kind-hearted and well-meaning people have asked me some variation of "What's the worst part about having cancer?" since I was diagnosed with incurable brain cancer in May.

I do not doubt the sincerity of their curiosity and hearts.

Was it the exhaustion? The hair loss? The occasional metallic taste? Not being able to drive or drink adult drinks? My skin itching from the radiation treatments? The feeling like a walking pharmacy from all the pills I now take?

Yet the question was still strange.

First, because the answer is clearly right there in the question:

"What's the worst part about having cancer?"

Having cancer is the worst part of having cancer.

Also, how does one quantify, or qualify, or weigh or measure the impact of such a thing? Especially someone who was extremely healthy before cancer leaped shockingly and unexplainably, into my life.

For the sake of my own mental health, I have tried (but admittedly failed a few times) to follow the sage advice from everyone from my doctors to my wife, our children, dear friends, family near and far, coworkers and even general acquaintances:

Do not dwell on how or why I got cancer. There is no answer. Sometimes crap – including cancer – just happens.

For a guy like me, the worst part is the weight of this burden on those around me. But even that is a hard measure since everyone, out of kindness and love, keeps telling me that there is no burden. They want to be part of my healing journey.

Then, like the cancer itself, a fairly accurate gauge suddenly and unexpectedly appeared.

My 4-year-old granddaughter, Riley Jean Williams.

Please understand this is not common parental or grand-parental pride speaking when I say, Riley is particularly astute, aware, and intuitive. I make my living around children and adolescents. What's more, I have two sharp, successful young adult daughters. So, I know from whence I speak.

From the start of this adventure, Riley has asked questions.

First, it was about the humongous black eye (actually, a beautiful shade of purple!) I had after surgery to remove a lemon-sized tumor and growth from my head. "Papa, how is you eye?"

It was about the Frankenstein's Monster-like scar on the side of my head. "Papa, how's you boo-boo?"

Then, about my general health. "Papa, you feel better today?"

Recently, our daughter, Emma, warned us that she and her husband, Jake (two fantastic young parents) had been talking to Riley about my condition.

They were purposely avoiding certain words like "cancer," "radiation," and "chemo" so as to not scare or confuse her. They wanted us to all be on the same page since Riley spends a lot of time with my wife and me. Very smart.

Then, most recently, Riley asked me if the medicine I was taking was making my hair fall out. Emma said Riley was very concerned because she was also taking medicine for the effects of a minor bout of Covid.

I have to say: that one conversation broke my heart.

I quickly explained that Papa is taking a different kind of medicine, and she didn't have to worry about her beautiful hair.

Then I handed the phone to my wife as tears welled and my throat tightened.

I admit, having been raised Catholic, I have a terrible case of Catholic Guilt. I feel horrible that I have put yet another potato on anyone's plate – emotional, physical, financial, psychological.

My rational mind knows I did nothing to "cause" or "deserve" brain cancer. Still, my whole personal and professional life has been about easing the burdens in other people's lives, not adding to them.

It's one thing to know that adults are upset about the many ways cancer has (and may yet) change my life, and theirs by association. And to know you have somehow caused (or at least

137

contributed to) the emotional burden of people you love and respect and care for.

But it is quite another to hear such thoughts from innocent children.

Still, the adults at least typically have enough Life under their belts to reasonably expect them to know what this all means.

I know this is a forced equation. So, I respectfully ask any mathematicians who may be reading this to go easy on me. Here goes:

Riley weighs 41 delightful, joy-filled, smiling, laughing, bossy pounds ("Papa, you come play hide and seek with me!")

So, I guess we can say that her confusion, concern, and potential for grief may be 41 times worse than most anyone else besides my wonderful wife and equally amazing daughters. At least for now.

But I hope and plan to emerge victorious from these dark woods.

Then, Riley's joy may be proportionately 41 (or more) times greater.

To everyone who has held my hand, prayed for me, sent wonderful messages of love, gifts, etc. – and to my beautiful granddaughter, the center of my world – I promise to do everything I can to win.

After all, there's a lot more hide-and-seek to play.

THE NEW NORMAL NEXT UP

By James Moore

Some of us are wondering when we will return to normal. We must understand though we're not returning to "normal." We can't return to a place we never left. Normal isn't set in stone. The one enduring trait about normality is its evolution. Normal continues to prove the adage "the more things change the more they stay the same."

Yet some still speak of returning to "normal" as in the pre-2020 Covid-19 era world. Others talk about the new normal. However, the next normal is upon us. The likelihood of returning to pre pandemic era ways is akin to going back to the 2019 calendar year. So as not to debate the point endlessly, I have come up with seven proposals for the back to normal crowd to make their case:

Proposal #1
If you want to tell someone "normal" will return, give them a call on the nearest pay phone that you find outside.

Proposal #2
It's always a good ideal to state your point in person. So, while you're at the gas station tell this to the gas station attendant who wipes your windows after she fills up your gas tank.

Proposal #3
It's a good strategy to continually make your point within your mind. You can do this while thumbing through your copy of the Yellow Pages.

Proposal #4
If you're not comfortable speaking up, just have your middle school student/child grandchild other explain your position in a handwritten (i.e.) cursive note.

Proposal #5
Those of you employed at a real physical workplace i.e., non-virtual can make their argument to coworkers as you stand in line at your job's HR office while waiting for your paper paychecks to be handed out to you at the end of the week.

Proposal #6
Include this in your social life. Discuss back to normal with your date before, during or after the movie you watch at the area's drive in theatre.

Proposal #7
Shop and chat. State your position about going back to normal to other bargain hunters while shopping at your local K-Mart. Better yet go to a nearby Sears store and do the same. There you have it, seven super ways for someone to make their case about a return to normal. No need to thank me. I'm just glad to help.

THE PAWN GUY AND THE DYSLEXIC VAMPIRE

By Ed Calkins

The second civil war isn't going well. Can we just all agree on that much? Look, I don't want to argue about the where and why of things. It's pointless. Both sides agree that there are facts and lies. Where we disagree about is which set of believes are which. It's all about where you get your news, what you consider education is, and what soda you drink, right? Mostly...well overwhelmingly, you're in one camp or the other, but I don't think anyone likes how it's played out in the United States.

The war started in 2036, of course when Congress, in spectacular show of internal hostility, passed a unanimous declaration of war, but years led up to that. Of course there was the 2020 election... can I mention that without reigniting arguments? I guess not.

Let's not get into it. Half of us believe that the mainstream media continues to lie about the 'steal' and the public schools are brainwashing our children...pumping them will lies and trying to make them diabetic by legalizing Pepsi. Or you believe it's the Conservative cable networks that are lying, and its private schools doing the brainwashing and diabetes is an invention of Coke.

Let's not go there. Let's just say that the election didn't start a war even though some claim there was a protest on the capital that amounted to an insurrection; others claim it was just a protest with liberal activist posing as reporters and lying to the public in an attempt to win political favor. Whatever you believe, one guy came in as president, and the other left which is as fortunate as things would ever get going forward. There were some extremist movers who made noise about taking the country by force, but for the most part, people who thought the election was stolen mostly responded to the problem by passing legislation at the State level to fix the election process. The people who didn't believe the first election was stolen thought the legislation was fixing the next election.

Then came the midterms elections for Senate and House congressmen. Please, please...let me continue without interruption. I'm not going to say if I think the elections were fair or legal, but you can't ignore that one hundred thirty senators got elected or reelected when there was only one hundred seats to fill. In the house, 583 representatives came to fill 435 seats, making chamber furniture a government issue when congressmen and congresswomen tried to sit on each other's lap. Voting on bills became a rare occurrence in those days as the 'who sits in what chair' issue was debated by force and in every case, ended in surrounding hospitals and leaving too few to call a vote.

Two years later, elections happened at all levels of government. Two incumbent presidents (one current, one former) declared victory. Although the election results were never certified in the senate because too few senators were not hospitalized, the now one hundred sixty five senators all cried foul, but disagreed on party lines on who did the fouling. Nor was either man sworn in, as the Supreme court justices boycotted the inaugural events which happen in two different locations along the Las Vegas strip. The Chief Justice, who was still a minor, claimed his opposition was apolitical, but his parents would let him make the trip.

Anyway, with two commanders-in-chiefs issuing contradictory orders, the U.S. military thought it imperative to immediately implement its invasion of Antarctica. Rumors had the Secret Service and other government institution joined forces to put down the Penguin insurgency lest the bird rebels eat all the fish.

That's when things started to get strange. It seemed like the Democratic president lost his office in a high stakes poker game and Bernie Sanders took his place. The Republican president also had some unknown monetary setback and sold his party (he claimed to own it) to the Coca-Cola corporation for a mere 46 trillion pounds (we won't get into why Trump won't accept U.S. dollars). Almost immediately after the Occupy Pepsi movement overtook that corporation and the vast majority of the democratic party. Both parties quickly added the merits of their corresponding soft drinks to their platforms, making which cola you preferred a highly charged political issue. To the chagrin of other corporate products, a demand that they take a side, and align with one party or the other under the peril of boycott soon sounded. GM, Twitter, General Mills, and Mars, to name a few all went right. Ford, Facebook, Quaker and Hershey's went left. Soon you could tell what a person believed by what they bought. Even sports began to splinter. Auto racing, wrestling, and boxing went right. Football, Basketball, and Hockey went left. Baseball was able to split itself down the middle, though it didn't go well and many teams lost fans. The American League went right, the National league went left. Even Little League had to decide team by team if a pitcher batted or not by the politics of its neighborhood.

Still, the nation pretended to be the United States and volent attacks had mainly congressmen as victims and perpetrators. There were some reports of the two presidents slapping at each other over bedroom assignments, but if we say any more, we're going to start arguing again and I'll never get to the declaration of war and what it has to do with a pawn shop. To that end, let's fast forward to 2034 when the Supreme court justices, who hated each other almost as much as they hated Congress, issued a ruling that they would declare ANY law from Congress or ANY executive order unconstitutional until one or both bodies could put forth a plan to reunite the country.

Bernie and Donald weren't going to do it, they were still boxing each other in their underwear. With inflation at 500 percent, public schools and pistols being banned or required, and essential government services becoming a rarity, Congress dug in and came up with a plan. The nation would go to war with itself. "…And therefore, it behooves every true American to kill any enemy within the U.S. borders who disagrees with his or her own political views until there is no disagreement that survives."

The first and last battle of the second Civil War, fought by Congressmen in their respective chambers was short and pathetic. There were some scratches and scrapes, but most casualties were heart attacks. With the battle inconclusive, the two parties retreated into differing headquarters to form a government in exile and hiding until such time when the citizens that supported them would inform them of their total victory as well as the problem of over-population being resolved.

Of course, that never happened. The second Civil War never got the amenities that no internal war should be without. The first and foremost was opposing armies as the U.S. armed forces were still patrolling icebergs. Second, there were no battles. People were as angry as ever at the other side, but no one wanted to kill anyone. Rifle merchants had disappointment, year after year, as shootings rose to only 600 per cent. When there was a shooting, it wasn't a battle. Some deranged soul, wanting to be a hero, would grab a gun and shoot a bunch of people at a mall or church till the ammo ran out or some other person subdued him. No one thought of that as victory in battle. Nor were there battle lines as all fifty states and all U.S. territories had people aligned in the minority. There was no leadership to speak of either. At the state and local level, the two parties had radicalized and ruled as if the other didn't exist. If you drank Coke, you'd vote at one poll site where you could choose between the Proud Boys or the Oath Keepers. If you drank Pepsi, it was either the Crips or the Bloods. The Divided States of American might have been split down the middle, but fighting wasn't fixing it as Congress had hoped.

No, people don't want to kill each other, they just want the other side to stop lying, but how does one do that.

Now, we can finally get to the pawn shop and how disappointed the old vampire was when he saw that it was still open, and the valuable manuscript was still in his possession.

It wouldn't be for long, the vampire knew. Already, the sign; "Everything Must Go – Name Your Price- No Reasonable Offer Will Be Refused" hung in the only shop still doing business in the ghost town that had been Las Vegas.

The man inside was the pawn shop owner, but he used to be the employer of over one hundred workers. It was sad to close when the business had been doing so well. But Lake Meade had dried up, and there wasn't any water. Gee, no water in a desert, who would have thought... He was sure it was the fault of the other side that drank the wrong cola. He'd be able to prove it too if he only had the money.

Only six weeks ago, when Vegas was still Vegas, did he come in to look over the items the overnight shift had bought and found a flowerpot with a strange plant inside.

"It's a Lie Detector plant," his employee promised, setting it on the counter where it was stay until the store closed its doors for the last time.

Well, the question, 'how much' got that employee fired. He regretted it now. The flower part of the plant changed colors when anyone spoke. It took a while, but not too long for the pawn shop owner to realized that color change was based on the candor of the speaker. It didn't just detect lies. It could distinguish exaggerations, fanciful wishes, half-truths, and ironies in their various degrees. It could even detect when a speaker was lying to oneself. It could even tell the difference between what a speaker knows to be true and what a speaker strongly believes. Doing business with this plant made negotiations foolproof and guaranteed he sold and bought at the best price. Of course, it was well worth the small fortune he paid. But what if he could grow more plants? What if every lying reporter had to admit that this story or that was a total fabrication for political gain?

"You'd be able to end the second Civil War." An old white breaded, pot-bellied, grump told him unkindly as if he was returning merchandize that hadn't worked as promised. The shop keeper did not see him coming in.

"Can I help you?" The Pawn Guy (as he liked to call himself) asked, glancing at the plant to make sure he could see it.

"You can help me by stop making the same mistake over and over, each time I come here!" He demanded.

"I've never seen you before."

"You've seen me plenty! You saw me tomorrow and every day after that for nearly a three year! Each time you bar me forever stepping foot in you shop! But I'm warning you, if you don't come to your senses and agree to get rich, you're going to see me again yesterday!"

The bewildered shop owner looked at his plant, hoping for some opinion.

"You're right," the customer told him. "The Soul Flower can detect many subtleties, but it can't detect insanity. You can be sure that I'm being truthful, but you can't assume I'm sane. I'm not by the way. My psychosis is the first of its kind…Deep Time psychosis, it's called. It's caused by time traveling too often while being a vampire…well, that plant there is calling that as an oversimplification but I'm quite sure you don't want the whole story. Ed Calkins is the name and psychosis, dyslexia, and newspaper delivery are my claim to fame. I'm also a truth telling vampire, as the soul flower will attest."

The plant seemed to agree.

"So, look," the pawn guy began as he tore his eyes away from the disappointing plant to give his best performance as a defeated beggar. "I don't want any trouble here but I'm trying to close the store; so I don't have to move all this stuff. I'm not interested in anything you have to make me rich, but I will sell you anything in the store for less than I paid.

"You're lying."

The vampire pointed at the plant. The coloring was strange. He hadn't told a boldfaced lie as only a few petals were completely red. The plant was acting like he was lying to himself. In that moment, the pawn guy wanted to know more about the nature of his lie than trying to make a profit. Looking at the pot he amended.

"Well, obviously I'm not going to sell anything for less than I paid for it unless I really have to."

The plant flagged that as completely true.

"And I don't want any trouble."

Also true.

"And the last thing I want to do is buy more stuff."

That was an exaggeration, but the plant mostly agreed.

"Maybe the lie is that you're not interested in anything I have to make you rich," the customer suggested. "Don't you think it's more that you're very interested, but you doubt I have anything you want to buy."

The plant seemed to think it was a possibility.

"Well, right now, I can't think of anything that I'd be willing to buy no matter how good the price."

146

That was a boldface lie. Both the plant and pawn guy knew it.

"You'd buy another soul flower in a second. And you'd pay everything you own and call it a bargain."

"How did you know that's what I was thinking?"

"I'm a vampire. I read minds…"

The plant started to waver.

"…it's just a don't read them well, you see. I'm dyslexic." Completely true.

"Well? Are you going to sell me another plant? Will you agree to trade everything I owed for it if you were?"

"No and no."

"Then the conversation about my buying something from you is over I sure."

"No again. But I'm here to help you get a whole greenhouse full of soul flowers. Think of how you could be the hero of the second civil war if you forced everyone causing it to tell the truth."

The flower agreed with all of it.

"Well…," the vampire paused trying to rise the suspense. "I so happen to have an original manuscript, the only one in existence… unless of course I go to my computer and print another copy."

"Just because it's rare doesn't mean its valuable."

"O but this one is. You see, I wrote it myself."

"And you're reasoning that a manuscript written by a vampire is collectable? Do you have some a letter of authenticity or some other proof that you wrote this while being a vampire? I didn't think so. Look, I'm sure it's very interesting and all but…"

The plant called out the sarcasm.

"Well, maybe you've read my other works. Have you read the novel 'Ruthless'?

"What? Another book about Bernie Sanders?"

"No! I made the whole thing up," claimed the vampire defensively. But the plant called his statement less the truthful.

"Ok. I tried to make the whole thing up. I wrote a story, sent it to my editor but she changed everything when she did an Ed-did-it."

"You mean an edit." The pawn guy was losing patience.

"Not the same thing."

"Ok, I know I'm going to regret this but what's the difference between an edit and an Ed-did-it?"

"I'm sure you know what an edit is like. These days, auto correct takes care of spelling and grammar. Mostly all you have to do is flag the sentences that don't make sense and change the words till they do."

The vampire seemed to think he was done explaining. Only when the faces of the pawn guy and the plant showed no understanding did he continue.

"Unless of course you're editing a manuscript and Ed did it. Remember, I'm famously dyslexic and psychotic, so when you read a sentence, the last thing you should do is change the words till it makes sense. You'll ruin the story. At first, my editor tried calling me and asking what the sentence should say, but I never recognized the text she was reading to me. So she got in the habit of changing it to what she thinks it should say. I don't read any better than I write...so I'm still reading my first book. I can't wait to find out how it ends."

"I'm sure you're exaggerating," the pawn guy stated. The plant didn't think that. "How many books did your editor edit."

"You mean Ed-did-it."

"Whatever."

"Well in the last book, I wrote very carefully as not to offend anyone. It was a bold new idea for me."

"And?"

"I seemed to have offended my editor. You see why this manuscript is so important? It's the first work with no Ed-did-it to take away its original meaning. Its full of wisdom that could make a guy like you rich enough to buy a whole green house of soul flowers that will end this civil war."

Without enthusiasm, the pawn guy ordered.

"Let's see the manuscript."

With that, a pile of computer paper shoulder high, materialized at the vampire's side. Without being prompted, he handed the pawn guy the title page on the top of the pile.

148

The pawn guy read it out loud.

"How a Porn Star Gets Rich."

"What?"

"Look, Mr. Vampire. Read the sign!"

The disgusted pawn guy pointed to his "No Politics Allowed in the Store." But that isn't what the confused vampire read.

"No pot-liquor alone in the store? I didn't bring any and I'm not alone."

The pawn guy couldn't hold back a laugh. Even the plant started pitching back and forth.

"That word is 'politics'."

"Are you sure? Wow. That sure changes the meaning of newspapers I've been reading. It hurts my feelings by-the-way when you laugh at me."

"Sorry, but I'm not interested in another book about Stormy Daniels."

"This book has nothing to do with the hurricane scandal Donald Trump got in before he was president. I still don't get that one."

"Stormy Daniels was the stage name of a porn star." The pawn guy told him chuckling.

"No," the vampire laughed. "That's too crazy. Are you saying that...Wait. That kind of makes sense. Wow. I though porn stars had more class. Anyway it make more sense than that monetary-lend- wind-ski thing that Clinton got impeached for. But wait. The manuscript has nothing to do with porn stars. It should say 'How a Pawn Store Gets Rich' and that's what its about...as in this one. The wisdom in this document in priceless. Please! I don't want to keep coming here and I'm running out of time. If you don't buy this then I'll just come back yesterday like I've done every day for the future three years. Every time you look the papers over, offer a price, but then kick me out and bar me from the store. I'm running out of yesterdays to come here because if I sell you the manuscript before the leprechaun sells you the soul flower, you'll never know I'm telling the truth!"

"Leprechaun! Is that what sold my night shift the plant? You do seem to know a lot about it? Will this manuscript tell me how to find that leprechaun?"

"No. But it's not needed. Get rich from the wisdom in it and the leprechaun will come back to you."

The plant agreed, but it never could account for 'crazy'. The pawn guy was just as tired of this 'here and now' as the vampire was of 'yesterdays'. What was the right question to ask to end this discussion?

He thought of one.

"What makes you think this manuscript will make me rich? Is there someone you know that's willing to pay a fortune for it?"

"Yes! Future you! Trust me, fifty years from now when you're a hero and everyone wants to interview you; you'll tell them you still don't believe how cheap it was to become the first zillionaire."

Nothing but agreement for the plant. Maybe the plant was crazy too. Another thought came. He mentioned cheap.

"Look. I don't know about any wisdom inside this pile of paper, and I'm sure I'm never going to sell this to someone who wants to read it, but the paper is recyclable. With paper shortage and inflation…I give you two grand for it."

"Fifteen."

"Fifteen? We're too far apart, but thanks for bringing it in.

"We're not apart at all." The old vampire insisted. "I want fifteen dollars…that's all. Keep the change as a tip. But! You have to promise to read the manuscript."

"Wait a second," The pawn guy growled. "That sounds very suspicious. Is this whole 'wisdom to get me rich' thing just a ploy by left leaning liberals to get me to switch soda drinks?"

He looked at the plant, waiting for his answer.

"No."

"Let me rephase. Does this manuscript have anything to do with politics?"

"No."

That was a lie, but before the pawn guy could kick him out the vampire amened.

150

"At least not any recent politics. No one is trying to change your soda drink. The only politics you'll find happened before the New World was discovered by Europe and 'soda' wasn't even invented.

That was true.

"Look. I'm going to ask again and I want to answer in a way that my plant can understand. Why do you think this manuscript will make me rich?"

"Because it's a map that leads to a treasure trove of articles, artifacts, and works of art to say nothing of precious metals. Actually the whole thing looks like ancient junk to me but to you…well you'll know how to change its value into current currency that leprechauns appreciate."

True.

"How do you know this?"

"I've seen the whole thing myself, with my own eyes. And anyone with legs can get there if they just read the manuscript. I've seen it myself."

It was true, but the speaker expected another follow-up question as if without that question it would be a half truth. The pawn guy noticed the pause in the vampire and his eyes on the plant.

"And?"

"And I didn't imagine it all, like I do sometimes. Look. I know I'm hard to believe. Somethings I image things and they just appear. Don't blame me for inflation though. I'm always very careful not to image currency. It's not me that minted too many thousand dollar bills! Ok, in the distant past, I might have over minted with my mind, but not this time. The treasure trove is real."

The plant agreed.

The pawn guy looked at the pile of paper and sighed.

"Do I have to read all of this to get to the 'getting rich' part?

The old vampire looked wounded but answered truthfully. "No."

"Show me the part that I do have to read. Show me the minimum."

The vampire dug from the middle of the stack and provided a single page. It was a map of some kind with a title.

The pawn guy looked it over.

"OUT!" he shouted, grabbing the government issued gun he was supposed to be using on anyone disagreeing with his politics. The defeated vampire slouched away.

The pawn guy thought about writing a new sign next to his 'No pot-liquor" one. This one would read 'no dyslexic crazy vampires' but he realized that he would have had to do it yesterday.

What he didn't realize is what the map was and what it was supposed to say. Neither did the vampire realize it said something other. What it said, 'Map to the Temporal Treason' was actually 'Map to the Templar Treasure'.

THE STRIPPER CAKE

By Steven James Cordin

Greer was pissed. The space inside the cake was too small for him. His legs were going to fall asleep if he didn't get out soon.

How the hell did strippers sit in these things for so long? He squatted inside the wooden cake shell, his hands clutching a pair of pistols. Of course, Greer was six foot five and well over two hundred and thirty pounds. He debated getting out and forgetting the whole thing. He couldn't breathe in the confined space and sweat ran down his back, a sensation he truly hated. His boss, Old Abe, did not pay him enough for this shit.

Three knocks against the shell caught Greer's attention. He recognized Trevino's muffled voice coming from outside. "It's time."

Finally. Greer let out a deep sigh. The cake shell lurched forward on its casters. Greer's left hand scrabbled along the inside of the shell to keep his balance. Crap, what a stupid idea. The pistol tumbled out of his hand, lodging between his knee and the inside wall of the shell, digging into his thigh. Greer ignored the pain and closed his eyes.

The music grew louder as he rolled forward, along with jeers and catcalls of the men at the party. Greer grabbed the pistol when the cake stopped moving. He smiled as the music began to change and a bunch of men joined in a loud offkey rendition of "Happy Birthday." This was a birthday surprise Tony and his boys would not forget.

He waited until the song died down and the catcalls resumed, then shot straight up. He ignored the pops in his knees as his head broke through the paper cap on the top of the cake shell. He glanced around at the dozen half-drunk men around the cake, their looks of lust changing to fear as they realized it wasn't a stripper popping out of the cake.

"Greer!" Tony, the birthday boy, blubbered, his eyes growing wide. He stood at the front of the group.

"Happy Birthday, Tony!" Greer rasped; his lips pulled back in a twisted grimace. Greer raised the pistols and squeezed the triggers.

Tony tried to run in three different directions at once and ended up falling backwards screaming.

The first blast of water from the pistols hit him in the face..

Greer grinned as he emptied the water pistols on to Tony. Most of the partygoers behind Tony began to laugh. A few not in on the gag stared. Tony cringed for a moment until he realized what happened. He sat in a puddle of water, not all of it from the water pistols, his jaw hanging open.

His eyes settled on Greer. "You son of a bitch!"

More laughter quickly erupted. A couple of the guys helped Tony to his feet. Greer stood there in the cake, shoulders quivering as he struggled to control himself. Tony glared at him for a few seconds. Greer watched as Tony lost the struggle not to break into a smile. He began to laugh with the others.

Greer waited till the laughter ended and raised his hands. "Boys, there is more fun across the hall. The girls are waiting!"

Greer stood in the cake shell as the others filed out and called Tony. "Hey! Come help me out of this thing."

"Christ you ape! I thought for a second Old Abe sent you to finish me off!"

Greer clutched Tony's arm as he climbed out of the cake. As he landed on his feet, he pulled Tony against him. Tony gasped as Greer's blade slid between his ribs. He pounded against Greer's chest a moment, and then went limp.

"Old Abe sends his warmest wishes, Tony." Greer whispered into Tony's ear.

Greer picked Tony up as if he weighed nothing and tossed him into the cake shell. Trevino, a small grey-haired man in a tan suit came in from the side door. Without a word, he pushed the shell out the door.

Greer walked over to the other banquet room. Better be sure none of the boys witnessed what happened to Tony. In the other room, the boys cheered at two topless blondes dancing to an old seventies tune.

Greer smirked to himself. Good. They haven't a clue.

As he headed to the exit, one of the partygoers called him. "Hey Greer! Where did Tony go?"

Greer looked over his shoulder. "He is checking out dessert."

THOUGHTS AT SUNRISE

By Holly Coop

If I didn't have a family
A job
Responsibilities day to day
Would I choose while in my bed
To simply stay

Without a force to motivate the actions I should take
Would my life just simply be
Hours spent
Without intent
Minutes ticking by
Every day a repeat of time

And would this space
be the place
I would choose to remain
If I didn't have a family
A job
Responsibilities day to day

It would seem a life's mundane
Is the thread to keep one sane
For without it
In my bed
I would remain

TUNNEL TO ROCKHOLD, AN EXCERPT FROM CIARA'S ISLAND

By Colleen H. Robbins

The western side of the tunnel to Rockhold.

An old lava tube, the tunnel to Rockhold was long and dark, lit by infrequent torches along the way. At least it ran straight. Half a dozen breaks in the tube's surface led to unlit tunnels at an angle to the main stretch. When the group woke, Nicholas reminded them that they must hurry through because the gates at each end of the tunnel closed at sunset. They started through, the tiniest pinpoint of light showing the distant exit. The breeze followed them, carrying the smells of the green valley behind them. Nicholas pointed out places where the ceiling appeared to drip. As they grew hungry near midday, the breeze stopped altogether, and as they traveled through the afternoon it reversed and brought pleasant smells of Rockhold cooking to torture them as they traveled. They picked up the pace. Nicholas limped more and more as they approached the exit from the tunnel.

"We can stop for a while and let you rest," Alaan suggested.

"No. We need to get through before they close the doors at sundown. Helps keep the plains-cats out. My leg's been bleeding again since lunchtime, and I've probably attracted every plains-cat in the Midlands into the tunnel by now. We have to go faster." He limped on ahead.

They could see figures in the distance, guards moving back and forth patrolling the tunnel exit.

When they could see the guards faces clearly, one of the guards turned to them, waving his hands. "RUN! It is almost time!"

"You heard him. RUN!" Nicholas sprinted ahead, stumbled, and fell. Alaan picked him up and continued ahead. Greta followed with the hatchlings and the women.

The guard frantically motioned them forward.

Nicholas wiggled. "Alaan, put me down. Get everyone else to safety. Run ahead now. Greta, stay here."

Alaan sprinted ahead, pulling Yasmine.

Ciara ran, urging the hatchlings to fly and glide.

Nicholas looked at Greta. ***Can you carry me?***

What? What do you mean?

Are you strong enough to carry me and fly? If you can't, I understand. Either way, fly to the exit now

I can try

Nicholas climbed up the dragon's side and sat on the saddle-shaped scale above her wings. He held on carefully, fully aware of her sharp scale edges, and unwilling to lacerate his hands. His legs bled enough already.

Greta ran and hopped, locking her wings to glide.

Careful, the ceiling is not very high

Nicholas looked ahead. The others had reached safety, the guards pulling them from the tunnel end. Alaan tried to come back, but another guard hauled him away.

Twenty feet to go, and the huge oaken doors started to move. Four guards with spears stood a body length apart as the exit narrowed.

Close your wings and run, Greta.

The dragon landed in a bounce, hopped, and squeezed through. Something flashed past just before the doors closed with a thunderous bang.

A guard fell backwards just in front of Greta, then scrambled away. "Another dragon! Get to shelter!" His spear skittered away, landing near Alaan. A plains-cat crouched nearby, eyes on the fallen guard.

"I've got this." Alaan scooped up the spear and ran towards the cat.

Greta didn't wait. She walloped the cat's shoulder with her tail and sent it spinning away from the guard.

Alaan shouted and waved for the cat's attention. The cat rolled to its feet and leapt to the attack.

Yasmine screamed.

Alaan fell to his knees, the butt of the spear braced against his leg as he held the point up at an angle.

The cat slammed into the spear, the point sliding up and between the ribs. The cat continued to slide down the spear shaft. It got a foot down on the ground and pushed.

Alaan fell over backwards.

The cat grabbed him with its claws and collapsed.

Nicholas limped forward. "Get it off him! He can't breathe!"

Before the guards could move, Greta lumbered over and shouldered the cat. It shifted sideways, uncovering Alaan's head.

Nicholas reached the cat, followed by the guards, and they pulled a gasping Alaan out from beneath its body.

His shoulders and upper arms were pierced by the cat's claws, and his forearm was lodged sideways in its mouth. Alaan looked up at the guards surrounding him. "A little help? I'm kind of tangled up."

USAID

By Sharon Houk

The blue jay doesn't stick around to eat. He balances a peanut in his beak and flies it too somewhere else. The nuthatch eats here - almost as if he had a napkin. The blue jay shoves his way around. The nuthatch waits his turn. The blue jay is big and upright. The nuthatch is small and upside down. The white patch on a nuthatch takes its turn. The wings of the blue jays are bullies. The blue jays are in the military. The nuthatches are in the State Department. Blue jays squawk. Nuthatches sing. This morning I put out lots of sunflower seeds and no peanuts.

WATERMELONS

By Denise M. Baran-Unland

To celebrate, Grandpa Clyde dug up the first watermelons ever grown on Fisher Farm, hauled them in a wheelbarrow to the fields where the girls were weeding, and then sent Robbie to fetch Mrs. Fisher and the little girls.

"Oh my! Oh my!" Mrs. Fisher exclaimed at the sight of the juicy scarlet flesh, laid out across the makeshift table of boards and sawhorses and practically begging to be eaten.

WHACK!

Mr. Munson's saw knife split the watermelon and rapidly fabricated it into slices.

Grinning at Mrs. Fisher, Grandpa Clyde brought forth another melon.

WHACK! Mr. Munson quickly chop-chopped.

Grandpa Clyde grabbed the largest wedge. "Here, Maybelle."

"Uncle Clyde, I can't...it's not my place..."

"Now, Maybelle. Your hungry girls are pining for their first bite."

"But..."

"So please respect the tender conscience of an old man, and decide if his first attempts are worthy of consumption."

WHACK!

"Clyde, you're too polite," Owen said over another WHACK! "Maybelle, eat the damn thing already. I, for one, don't intend to languish."

"Well..."

All eyes watched Maybelle as she bit into the tender rosy flesh. The look on her face wasn't enjoyment.

It was rapture.

"Anything like Mississippi watermelons?" Grandpa Clyde reached for large chunk and gestured for the girls to follow.

"Mmm, hmmm."

Mrs. Fisher devoured the watermelon, expertly spat out the seeds to the astonishment of the girls, and frantically licked her fingers.

The slices disappeared as fast as Mr. Munson cut them, with Mr. Munson eating more than any two people, although Robbie gnawed wedge after wedge to the rind with the speed of a hardworking beaver.

"We're spoiling our appetites for supper," Maybelle wiped her dripping chin with her sleeve.

"So we spoil our appetites." Mr. Fisher stole another slice. "We'll have bread and cheese and no kitchen clean-up."

Bryony spat seeds with the rest and wondered how Reverend and Mrs. Parks might react if they could see her acting so common. Susan consistently sprayed farther than anyone, a feat that didn't escape Mr. Munson as he chopped the watermelon.

"Clyde," Mr. Munson sighed. "I haven't seen seed-spitting this fine since the time we turned an entire city against us because of our watermelons."

"A likely story," Daisy said.

"What! Clyde, you never told these beautiful young ladies about our magnificent watermelon patch?"

"Must've slipped my mind."

Daisy still looked skeptical. "You're making it up."

Mr. Munson slapped his hand to his chest. "Upon my beating heart, Miss Daisy, I swear, I'm telling the truth. Now if everyone will gather under that white bush yonder," he pointed to a Japanese lilac, "while I polish off the last of this delectable melon, I will share our strange tale. Clyde, if I forget a detail or two, feel free to chime in."

"Whatever you say, Owen."

Bryony eased onto the grass. Her stomach rolled like waves in the lake. Shallow breaths were safer.

Maybelle reclined against the tree and clasped her hands over her huge abdomen, Marigold curled up near her legs and pillowed her hands.

Daisy plucked grass; Lilac panted through gaping mouth; Ivy silently gagged; Rose clenched her fists and closed her eyes.

162

"My tummy hurts," Heather announced.

Mr. Fisher faced the bean fields and hugged his knees.

Robbie was snoring. Susan was petting Blue.

Mr. Munson spat out the last seeds and then sprawled beside Clyde, who lay on his back and watched the clouds.

"It was the winter of eighteen something, January, I think, and your Grandpa Clyde and I were footin' around back east. On a whim, we bought a big ol' field that was going cheap. And on that field was a little green house. Now, what do you suppose we found in the cellar?"

"Watermelons," Heather said.

Mr. Munson tweaked her cowgirl hat. "Wrong! There were turnips and rutabagas and potatoes, and pickles and preserves that weren't as good as your ma's and apple cider that was far, far, far better than your Grandpa Clyde's."

"Thanks, Owen."

"So your Grandpa Clyde said to me, 'Owen, we could live like kings off the rations until spring,' and I said, "Clyde, we could.' So we set up the checker board and didn't budge for three months, except to venture into the cellar for more cider and provisions."

"What about firewood?" Ivy asked.

"Didn't I mention firewood? "

"No," Daisy said.

"Oh. Well, there was a huge stack in the cellar. We had plenty all winter."

"And meat?"

"Miss Daisy, we had plenty of meat. Any critters sneaking into our basement and hoping to winter with us was skewered and roasted over the fire. That job fell to your Grandpa Clyde, because he kept losing at checkers."

Grandpa Clyde snickered and slid his hat over his face.

"Finally, the only item left in the cellar was a burlap sack."

"A body!" Daisy cried excitedly.

"Watermelon seeds!"

"Wha...watermelon seeds?"

"Miss Daisy, those watermelon seeds gave us the best summer of our lives. We planted, hoed, weeded, and by summer we had splendid watermelons: dark green on the outside and crimson-red on the inside, with seeds so black they looked like flecks of the devil's soul."

A snort broke out under Grandpa Clyde's hat.

"Now what do you think we did?"

"Ate them?" Heather asked.

"Ate them? We sold them!"

"Oh."

"Hundreds and hundreds! Nobody had seen fruit so sweet and ripe. Everyone spent so much on watermelon and giving away prizes for seed-spitting contests, the town went broke. The officials called an important meeting and unanimously passed a law against selling watermelon, and do you know why?"

No one answered.

"Because they said it was the devil's fruit, and everyone knows the devil's fruit causes frightful shakes and aches."

"You had to stop?" Lilac whispered.

Mr. Munson's face softened.

"Miss Lilac, it takes a lot more than a silly law and fever or two to stop your Grandpa Clyde and me."

Bryony glowered at the grass.

"For every watermelon we moved out of that field, we set a mossy boulder in its place. Day by day, the townspeople grew more frightened of our field. On July nineteenth an angry mob showed up. And that," Mr. Munson crossed his heart, "is the very last time I tasted watermelon. Until today."

Ivy's eyes opened wide. "Were you hurt?"

"They set fire to our watermelon field, but your grandpa and I were already an easy mile away, each of us carrying a sack of money and a sack of watermelon seeds. But we did stop to watch the thick smoke overtaking the sky. Foolish townspeople!"

Mr. Munson ruefully shook his head.

"Because they didn't understand watermelons?" Rose asked

"Because they kept growing their fire, bigger and bigger, until it reached the candle factory, where they stored the saltpeter. The explosion destroyed the town. All they had left was a burnt field of rocks."

164

"If that's true," Daisy said, "why didn't it make the papers?"

"It did make the papers, well, all except the watermelon part. And who can blame them?"

"I'm glad you and Grandpa Clyde got away."

"That we did, Miss Lilac, although..."

Mr. Munson shifted his gaze over the quivering form of Grandpa Clyde.

"Although, what?" Daisy asked.

"I don't know, Clyde. Is it wise to tell them?"

Grandpa Clyde removed his hat. His eyes were merry. "Owen, you've gone this far..."

Mr. Munson leaned in. "Can you keep a secret?" he whispered.

They nodded.

"We never spent our watermelon money. Eventually, they brought the town back to life and built big banks smack over our old watermelon field. So we invested our money in those banks."

"Why? Stupid, mean town."

Grandpa Clyde sat up. "Daisy, a good farmer always puts his money back into his field. And speaking of fields, Owen."

On cue, Robbie awakened and rubbed his eyes.

Mr. Munson sprang to his feet, swept off his cowboy hat, and bowed low.

"Alas, my toils are not yet complete. And so, adieu, adieu, adieu!"

Robbie disassembled the "table." The other three men headed to the fields: Mr. Fisher with his hands in his pockets; and Mr. Munson laughing, joking, and slapping Grandpa Clyde on the back.

ZOOKEEPER

By Kathy Carberry

"We're getting outta here." Trace held up her two hands and Alex gave her a high five. The bad part was, they wouldn't be going to the same place. They were together in juvey for two years, and even law-abiding besties couldn't be closer. But they were both tough and neither was about to get sentimental even at a time like this.

"Don't be dumb and wind up here again." Alex said. It was her attempt at being wise.

"Hey, no way you'll be back here. Right?" Trace smiled when she said this. She really did wish her friend the best, but she had her doubts. Alex was a wild card.

"Don't worry, I just won't get caught again. Where are they sending you?"

"To the zoo." Trace held the idea close, she really lucked out. She always loved the zoo ever since she was a little kid. Now she would go there and be a zookeeper, well sort of anyway.

"You're lucky. I'm going to some old folk's home. I'm gonna be bored out of my mind, that's for sure." Alex shook her head and looked at the floor. "Take care of yourself Trace. Maybe I'll see ya around some time." Trace felt at home as soon as she got to the zoo. She admitted it if you asked her, but the place gave her a sense of belonging. It was early in the morning. She looked up at the sky. Clear and blue. There was a soft warm breeze. It felt good on her skin.

One of the assistants. Ally or Elly, or whoever was assigned to showing her around. Ally or Elly kept her distance. She was just some goody two shoes who kept glancing sideways at Trace as if she was expecting her to hit her over the head and take the pretty silver bracelet. She kept twisting it, always keeping a hand on it to make sure it was still there.

"Nice bracelet you're wearing. I used to steal ones like it." Trace said, a big grin spread across her face. Seeing the look on Ally, Elly's face was priceless. That ended the tour fast. To bad Ally, Elly wasn't keeping her hand in her pocket. That's where the real treasure was. Ally, Elly, lead Trace to the office where she pointed out the uniforms and supplies for cleaning. With that done, Trace was on her own.

Some of the animals were out. The zoo would be opening in ten minutes. Trace walked the perimeter. She scooped up stray pieces of garbage and dumped it in cans that were scattered all around. Nothing big just a few wayward scraps and cups.

People started trickling in and her cheeks began to hurt from giving so many smiles and hellos.

Watching the little kids made her think about the last time she went to a zoo. It was before her dad skipped out and her mom started entertaining men for money. She remembered all the times her mom kicked her outside when a man was visiting. A few of them had even suggested adding her to the mix. Her mother wasn't opposed to the idea, and that's when Trace ran. She had to survive on her own on the streets for years, taking what she could until she got caught and sent to juvey. The place was never great, but it was a place to live. Now, she would have to spend every night in a group home. She had to go there as soon as she left the zoo. Maybe she could hide out when they closed and stay here where she felt at home already.

She wandered along keeping her eyes open for debris and people trying to climb fences. Occasionally, someone would ask her a question. If she didn't know the answer, she made something up. There was at least a small chance she was right.

She stopped in front of the tiger enclosure. They were both out, looking beautiful as they paced back and forth making eye contact with the crowd. It was a pretty good setup. They had their own play area and plenty of space to move around in. Still, Trace could see why some people didn't like zoos. The whole idea of confinement wasn't great. Still, it was a lot better than being in juvey.

She could smell the popcorn from the little cart and noticed the case of soft drinks right next to it. She was entitled to free snacks as part of the gig. She walked over and the lady running it smiled at her.

"Are you new honey?" The lady asked.

"Yeah." Trace said, looking away. She still didn't trust people.

She walked around munching the popcorn and sipping the soda. The broom and pan tucked under her arm. It may not have been the best time to eat. She had to clean out a few of the cages while the animals were outside. She hoped the smell wouldn't bring the popcorn and soda back up.

That night she decided she wasn't going to the group home. There would be nothing there but more of the same boring rules. She hid in a dark corner of the cat house until the place was empty. Finally, she had everything to herself. She made her way back to the tiger enclosure. Only one of them was still out. He must have hidden out too. They made eye contact.

She thought she heard voices, but how could that be? Everyone who could talk was gone for the day. But then it got louder...and closer. She hid behind one of the walls.

"We have to move them tonight. If we mess up, he'll have our asses." "Don't panic. You're always panicking. I'm back now." Someone else said.

The second voice sounded familiar. Trace scrunched up further into the wall and peaked out. She heard herself squeak. She put her hand over her mouth.

"Trace, what are you doing here. You're supposed to be at the home." It was Alex.

"Yeah, and where are you supposed to be? Not here that's for sure." Trace answered back.

Alex shrugged. "It's big business kid."0 She jerked her head to the guys behind her. They wore a lot of protective gear and were holding a large syringe. It didn't take long for Trace to put two and two together.

"No way!" She shouted. She was just about to stand in their way, but it wouldn't do any good. Then she noticed a small slot just large enough to fit a keycard. She pulled the one she swiped from Ally/Elly out of her pocket and slid it back and forth. A low door

168

swung open. It took the tiger no time to get out. Trace dodged out of the way. Alex and her goons weren't so lucky. She slipped the card back into her pocket. No one was going to hurt or steal the animals in this zoo while she was around.

DEDICATION

Write Where We Are: WriteOn Joliet Sixth Annual Anthology is dedicated to Eric Brumbaugh, who passed away September 6, 2022.

Members of WriteOn Joliet will miss Eric's presence, his talented writings, and his technical skill at hybrid meetings. Virtual meetings became more interactive after Eric created a drive for members to upload their writings, a drive known as:

Eric's Grand Google Room of Turkey and Fixings.

Eric's Magic Voodoo Machine.

Eric's Magical Fun Box of Literary Joy and Wisdom.

Eric's Valentine's Day Room of Googly Love,

Dr. Eric's Super Snake Oil and Magic Googly Moogly Drop Box

Googly Moogly Box of Love and Kindness.

Santa Eric's Secret Elf Workshop.

The special room behind The Magic Door of Joy and Mystery.

Eric's House of Google and Magical Page of Visions and Wizardry.

The second shelf up from the floor behind the pink piggie cookie jar in Eric's Google Room.

Eric: May you rest in peace and may your words be forever read

GONE TOO SOON

WriteOn Joliet lost two other members this year.
Amee Bohrer, one of WriteOn's founding members and a blogger
for many years, died June 14, 2022, at
the age of 41. Read her writings at
https://unrelentingamee.wordpress.com/

Jean Dunning, a freelance writer and photographer, known locally
for her fairy photography, died June 26, 2022
at the age of 55. View her photos at
https://www.facebook.com/photographsbyjeanne

BIOGRAPHIES

Denise M. Baran-Unland is the author of the BryonySeries supernatural/literary trilogy for young and new adults, the Adventures of Cornell Dyer chapter book series for grade school children and the Bertrand the Mouse series for young children.
She has six adult children, three adult step-children, fourteen total grandchildren, six godchildren, and four cats.

She is the co-founder of WriteOn Joliet and previously taught features writing for a homeschool coop, with the students' work published in the co-op magazine and The Herald-News in Joliet.

Denise blogs daily and is currently the features editor at The Herald-News. To read her feature stories, visit theherald-news.com. For more information about Denise's fiction and to follow her on social media, visit bryonyseries.com.

Ed Calkins is a real, 60-something, proud of his Irish-heritage computer programmer and amateur writer who has also spent his entire life working in newspaper circulation. Years ago, Calkins invented a "ruthless dictator" alter ego, also known as "The Steward of Tara."

With Calkins' permission, BryonySeries author Denise M. Baran-Unland furthered altered him to create a minor character in "Bryony," making Calkins the first Irish vampire of any significance. Of course, Calkins claims "Bryony" is really all about him, so he's held his own book signings, which he is calls, "The Ed Calkins Tour." There must be some truth in his sentiments, because Calkins' plot importance does grow with each novel in the original BryonySeries trilogy.

Calkins is the author of "Ruthless" (his backstory) and "Denise M. Baran-Unland's Irish Genealogy." He also shares his writings on the BryonySeries blog. Email him at bryonyseries@gmail.com.

Kathy Carberry there's not a lot to say about things in general. I raised three kids and have my first grandbaby on the way. I've held a wide variety of jobs because I have a short attention span. Except when it comes to reading and writing. I can do both for hours on end without stopping to look at any form of time device. I've had this affliction for as long as I can remember, starting around age six.

I was extremely fortunate to have parents who fed this need with very few limits. They didn't know the meaning of the word censorship. I was encouraged to read anything and everything my little heart desired, and they were always available for open discussion after I finished a book. I passed this same incredible gift on to my children, hopefully they are grateful. Unless I miss my guess, the legacy will continue to the next generation.

As for writing, I started a little later. Somewhere in the tween years. I wrote for myself and didn't show my work to anyone. Teachers praised my work at times, and it gave me a sense of pride, but I never considered truly taking it on. Now in my later years, I have an eye toward publication. I am a slow writer. I tend to demand perfection from myself, but not from others. This is a problem I am slowly but surely starting to overcome.

Holly Coop Touching hearts with words has become a life purpose to Holly Coop.

Coop writes and publishes inspirational poetry, motivational quotes, and spiritual insights. As the author of five poetry collections, Coop hopes her words will stir hearts and inspire others in their purpose. Coop also enjoys sketching, creating photo notecards and art, featuring her poetry. (hollycoopcards.Etsy.com).

At hollycoopauthor.wordpress.com, Coop shares reflections, nuggets of wisdom, and anything that comes to mind.

Coop resides in Joliet, Illinois with her husband, children, and furry friends.

Her poetry collections are available for purchase at: HollyCoopBooks.com, The Book Market Sales and Trading Center (Crest Hill, Illinois), Joliet Public Library, Amazon.com, BarnesAndNoble.com, and hollycoop.etsy.com.

Steven James Cordin usually lurks in the outskirts of Joliet, Illinois to pay the bills and bar tabs,

Cordin has worked in banking as a repo man, foreclosure guru, and fraud investigator.

He writes about fraud and crime as well as horror fiction. Cordin is currently working on a collection of crime fiction short stories.

Diana Estell The joy and pains of Estell's personal story, as well as her educational background, have shaped her writing style.

Estell has a Bachelor of Arts from Northern Illinois University and it was there, while writing for her classes in anthropology, that her love of writing re-awoke.

Growing up, Estell had a book in her hand constantly. Books like Little House on the Prairie, Little Women, and countless others. The love of words is a deep passion of hers. She enjoyed reading the dictionary, taking words and changing them into new words. Words were her imaginary playground, a veritable lush garden, springing out blossoms of creativity.

When Star Wars blasted into orbit, so too did Diana's love for all things fantasy. Dungeon and Dragons and Star Trek played a significant role in her private imaginary world. Now the worded playground, with its abundant flora, sprung forth thorns of sharpened steel. Planets and creatures emerged with ease. This passion for fantasy has never left but has grown stronger.

Estell has traveled extensively, most recently to Paris, France. Her love for history, martial arts and weapons is woven into her writings. She has a black belt in a martial arts blend of Taekwondo and Jujitsu.

She had anticipated she would be going on archeological digs after graduating, but childhood dreams never die. No matter how many layers of her past accumulated, nothing could stop a story from emerging in her mind.

Estell's first novel, *Abyss of the Fallen*, was released by Brimstone Fiction.

Email her at inklings67@aol.com

Robert B. Hafey resides in Homer Glen, Illinois. He is a retired operational manager who adds value to the world as a consultant, writer, photographer, passionate cook, world traveler, storyteller, husband, father, and grandfather.

His memoir titled, *Boomhood – A Baby Boomer's Free-Range Childhood*, contains generational childhood stories to which baby-boomers can relate.

His latest title, *Bumping and Snacking – Discovering a Worldview*, takes the reader on a fun journey of discovery. Self-planned travel experiences and food stories are used to uncover both the cultural differences, and the common qualities of people. Seeking to understand others to better understand who we are, is a journey worth taking.

Contact Hafey at roberthafey.com.

Tom Hernandez is a writer, public speaker, performer and communications professional. Born and raised in Joliet, Illinois, he has been writing personally and professionally since childhood. His writing explores the many complicated facets of life — marriage, family, relationships, identity, aging, parenting, faith, social justice and politics.

He has published five books of poetry, essays and fiction. He and his wife, Kellie have two adult daughters and welcomed their first grandchild in 2018. They live in Plainfield, Illinois. For more information, visit www.tomhernandezbooks.com.

Sharon Houk is a multidisciplinary artist and award-winning playwright. Her work has been seen in Coe Review, Rhino Fest, Irish American News, and the Billie Limacher Emerging Playwrights' Festival. Her much-anticipated debut novel is entitled Carrots Will Not Absolve You.

Lindsay Lake is a registered nurse with a degree in psychology. She worked with mentally ill adults, teens and children.

Born in Ohio, she has lived in the Midwest except for a fourteen year stint in California for college at Shasta College in Redding and

Sacramento State University. Governor State University in Illinois is her alma mater.

She started writing at age ten. An avid film buff even then, she rewrote movies. She said they weren't quite right, and she needed to make them perfect. In adolescence she wrote short stories, poems and lyrics for an all-girl rock band.

Lindsay published a fanzine over the 1990s, doing the editing, writing, photography, layouts plus interviews.

She has written three lengthy Avengers fanfiction novels and a Disney+ like serial, published on archivesofourown.org.

As a nurse she studied all systems of the human body and their functioning. No body part held her attention and fascination like the human brain and human behavior. Her characters are flawed and full of psychic complexity. As a feminist she writes to liberate her male characters from toxic masculinity for only then will the earth be free of aggression and war.

Inspired in 2019 by the 50th anniversary of the events of 1969, her current novel, "Flower Power" was written as an amusement over the pandemic. She wrote about everything missing from her life at that time: fun, adventure, excitement, crowded military barracks rooms, alpha males, laughs, travel, romance, intimacy and sex. Flower Power is available on Kindle as are two other novels, The Best Lay in Hollywood, and The Open Road.

She lives in Illinois, temporarily. She welcomes all correspondence. lindsaylake2001@yahoo.com.

Cean Magosky is new to WriteOn Joliet but has been writing for quite a while as a member of the Downers Grove Writers Workshop.

First exploring poetry, he switched to mostly short story and historical fiction.

As surgical nurse, Magosky has presented on the regional and national level and was a member of Northwestern Medicine Nursing Ambassadors for the Fine Arts and contributed to their project *Listening to Life*.

His children's story *Oatmeal Raisin Bear* was featured in The Herald-News' *LocalLit* series.

James Moore doesn't write because it's there. He writes because it's not there.

James brings his biblically centered outlook onto a variety of topics. He shares stories, poetry and other collections of words to a weary world of eyes that are hungry to read material that will entertain and/or enlighten their view.

To that end, James has made his creative endeavors available at jamescmo.com, the online community Medium.com and "how to" rideshare driving entrepreneurial articles on toughnickel.com.

Sue Mydliak lives in Illinois with her husband and has been writing for 10 years.

She started writing when the book "Twilight" first came out and fell in love with the paranormal genre.

Since then, she has written and finished her Rosewood Trilogy and just recently her anniversary edition, "Forever," which is the first book re-written for adults.

She has also published "Southern Shorts," which is an anthology of short stories about Dry Prong, Louisana and "Night Games," another paranormal novel.

For more information and to purchase her books and artwork visit suemydliak.wordpress and fineartamerica.comprofilessue-midlock

Colleen H. Robbins has been writing since a young age, and is the author of the Daraga series of high Fantasy books (Daraga's Quest, The Daraga's Children, Dark Protector, Ciara's Island). She has also released two short story collections (Stories of a Sheltered Suburbanite, Night Breeze and Moonbeams) and a middle grade book co-authored with Tarina Jameson (Return to Ganagar).

She currently resides in Joliet, IL after living in numerous other states. She likes to write science fiction, fantasy, and horror, but writes mainstream fiction as well.

Jennifer Russ is a freelance writer focusing on animal welfare and human rights. They are the author of "The Heart's Bone," a fictional account of Tibet's youngest self-immolators, and "Whitewallsville:

One Man's Journey Through Tigers, Frozen Birds, and Suicide," a story of grief and redemption set within the walls of a mental institution.

When Jennifer is not tackling the serious topics, they enjoy petting dogs, smelling old books, cosplay, and traveling the world.

Duanne Walton said: "Writing is my gift from God and it's been with me forever. It's seen me through rough times and brought me to WriteOn Joliet where I've found support, encouragement and friends.

"I've also discovered other talents as an intrepid videographer, interpretive dancer or mime, and comic strip writer artist. I am blessed and thankful."

Made in the USA
Monee, IL
04 November 2022

17103236R00104